STAR WARS™

THE CLONE WARS™

OFFICIAL EPISODE GUIDE

Written by Jason Fry

Published by Ladybird Books Ltd 2010
A Penguin Company
Sunbird is a trade mark of Ladybird Books Ltd

Penguin Books Ltd, 80 Strand,
London, WC2R 0RL, UK
Penguin Books Australia Ltd,
Camberwell, Victoria, Australia
Penguin Group (NZ), 67 Apollo Drive, Rosedale,
North Shore 0632, New Zealand
(a division of Pearson New Zealand Ltd)

www.penguin.co.uk

ISBN: 9781409390336

10 9 8 7 6 5 4 3 2 1

Printed in Slovakia

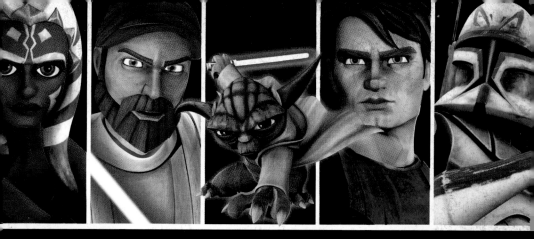

STAR WARS™

THE CLONE WARS™

OFFICIAL EPISODE GUIDE
SERIES 1 AND 2

SERIES 1

SERIES 2

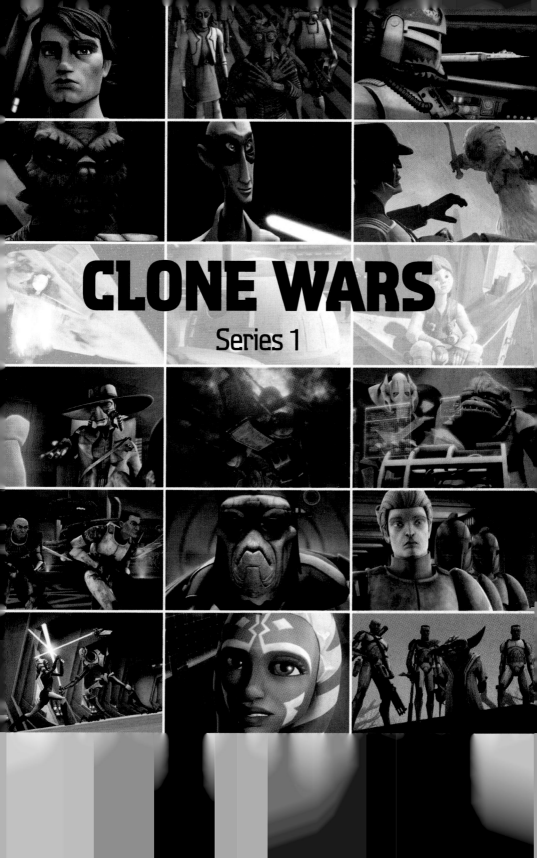

CLONE WARS

Series 1

SYNOPSIS

During the battle for Christophsis, Anakin and Obi-Wan are surprised when Anakin's new Padawan, Ahsoka, arrives. Together, Anakin and his new apprentice destroy a Separatist shield generator while Obi-Wan stalls the attacks by negotiating a fake surrender to General Whorm Loathsom.

After the Separatist defeat, Yoda sends Obi-Wan to meet with Jabba the Hutt, whose son, Rotta, has been kidnapped. Meanwhile, Anakin and Ahsoka head to the planet Teth to look for the missing Huttlet. However, it's a trap. Dooku arranged the kidnapping and plans to blame it on the Jedi. Asajj Ventress tries to stop the Jedi, but she fails and allows Ahsoka and Anakin to escape.

On Coruscant, Padmé pays a visit to Jabba's uncle, Ziro. She learns that he conspired with Dooku to kidnap the baby.

On Tatooine, Anakin and Ahsoka defeat Dooku and his MagnaGuards and bring Rotta to Jabba. The Hutt threatens to kill the Jedi, but frees them when he learns that his uncle was responsible for the kidnapping.

A PADAWAN WOULD JUST SLOW ME DOWN.

NEWSREEL

A galaxy divided! Striking swiftly after the Battle of Geonosis, Count Dooku's droid army has seized control of the major hyperspace lanes, separating the Republic from the majority of its clone army. With few clones available, the Jedi generals cannot gain a foothold on the Outer Rim as more and more planets choose to join Dooku's Separatists. While the Jedi are occupied fighting a war, no one is left to keep the peace. Chaos and crime spread, and the innocent become victims in a lawless galaxy. Crime lord Jabba the Hutt's son has been kidnapped by a rival band of pirates. Desperate to save his son, Jabba puts out a call for help – a call the Jedi are cautious to answer . . . ■

YOU'RE RECKLESS, LITTLE ONE. YOU NEVER WOULD HAVE MADE IT AS OBI-WAN'S PADAWAN . . . BUT YOU MIGHT MAKE IT AS MINE.

Obi-Wan Kenobi

Equally respected for his skill in battles and negotiations, Obi-Wan Kenobi was Anakin Skywalker's master until his Padawan passed the trials and became a Jedi Knight.

WEAPON PROFILE
Lightsaber

The weapon of a Jedi Knight, its hilt emits a blade of pure energy focused by a crystal.

ALIEN PROFILE
Togrutas

Togrutas evolved from predators, and their colourful skins were originally used to confuse prey. They have two hollow montrals growing from the top of the skull and "head tails" that fall over the chest and back. Togrutas preserve some of their native traditions as Jedi, wearing elaborate costumes and trophies.

PLANET PROFILE
Christophsis

Region: Outer Rim

Inhabitants: Humans, servant species

Christophsis is a world of crystal spires. Its people became immensely rich by mining asteroids in the system's outer reaches.

Captain Rex

A veteran of many battles, the elite clone Rex is Anakin Skywalker's gruff, no-nonsense second-in-command, and is as brave and headstrong as the Jedi he serves.

PLANET PROFILE
Teth

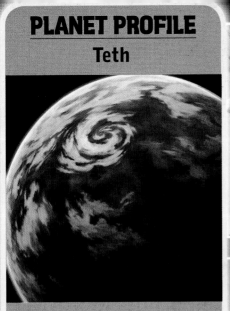

Region: Wild Space

Teth was first settled as a Hutt vacation spot, but abandoned after it became the scene of too many clan vendettas. It is dotted with abandoned monasteries and Hutt palaces.

ALIEN PROFILE
Hutts

Hutts are mighty amphibians that have controlled a large part of the galaxy for thousands of years, making handsome profits from shady businesses such as spice smuggling and slavery. Hutts are ruthless and greedy, and see themselves as the only species worthy of respect in the galaxy. Their clans compete ferociously over markets and the smallest points of honour.

EPISODE HIGHLIGHT

Jabba the Hutt

A crime lord of the Desilijic family, Jabba controls a number of Outer Rim trade routes. His support could help tip the Clone Wars to the Republic or the Separatists.

VEHICLE PROFILE
AT-TE

Model: All-Terrain Tactical Enforcer

Class: Walker

Weapons:
- Laser cannons
- Concussion warheads

VEHICLE PROFILE
Retail Droid

Properly known as LR-57 combat droids, these hulking droids like to bury themselves, wait for an enemy to walk overhead, and then explode out of the ground in ambush.

ALIEN PROFILE
Kerkoidens

Kerkoidens are known as clever traders and canny politicians. Many feel a bit embarrassed about their long claws and sharp teeth, and often take pains to appear as refined and sophisticated as possible.

VEHICLE PROFILE
Republic Attack Gunship

Model: Rothana Heavy Engineering

Class: Repulsorlift gunship

Weapons:
- Laser turrets
- Air-to-air rockets
- Missile launchers

EPISODE HIGHLIGHT

YOU'LL HAVE TO DO BETTER THAN THAT, MY DARLING.

Rotta

Rotta is Jabba's young son, and as cranky and smelly as one would expect a Huttlet to be. Jabba calls him his "pedunkee mufkin," and treats his son with rare tenderness.

"Great leaders inspire greatness in others"

SMALLER IN NUMBER WE ARE, BUT LARGER IN MIND . . .

SYNOPSIS

Jedi Master Yoda and a team of clone troopers have been sent to the system of Toydaria to convince the Toydarian King, Katuunko, to join the Galactic Republic. However, Count Dooku has sent the assassin Asajj Ventress to negotiate the Separatists' own deal with Katuunko. Above the moon of Rugosa, Yoda is ambushed by Separatist forces, sending the Jedi Master and his clone escorts into a race against time to defeat Ventress's droid army and prove the Republic's worth to King Katuunko.

Rys, Thire, and Jek

Members of the Coruscant Guard whose duty it is to protect Yoda on his diplomatic mission to Rugosa.

A galaxy divided by war! Peaceful worlds must choose sides or face the threat of invasion. Republic and Separatist armies vie for the allegiance of neutral planets. Desperate to build a Republic supply base on the system of Toydaria, Jedi Master Yoda travels to secret negotiations on a remote, neutral moon . . . ■

Asajj Ventress

Count Dooku's most trusted assassin. Though she's not officially a Sith apprentice, Ventress has clearly been well-trained in the arts of lightsaber duelling and Force manipulation.

EPISODE HIGHLIGHT

YOUR HELMETS, REMOVE THEM. YOUR FACES, I WISH TO SEE.

THERE'S NOT MUCH TO LOOK AT HERE, SIR. WE ALL SHARE THE SAME FACE.

DECEIVE YOU, EYES CAN. IN THE FORCE, VERY DIFFERENT EACH ONE OF YOU ARE.

VEHICLE PROFILE
Republic Frigate

Model: Refitted *Consular*-class cruiser

Class: Frigate

Weapons:
- Twin light turbolaser cannon batteries
- Point-defence medium laser cannons

The words at the top and bottom of the screen on Thire's macrobinoculars are written in Aurebesh, a common system for writing in the *Star Wars* universe. They read: "Infrared Mode" on the top and "Regular Mode" on the bottom.

I ASK, HOW CAN A JEDI PROTECT YOU IF THEY CANNOT PROTECT THEMSELVES?

TRIVIA

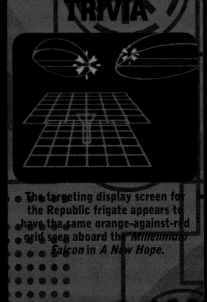

The targeting display screen for the Republic frigate appears to have the same orange-against-red grid seen aboard the *Millennium Falcon* in *A New Hope*.

King Katuunko

The ruler of the system of Toydaria and its moon Rugosa. The winged Toydarians' minds are able to resist all types of Jedi mind tricks.

DROID PROFILE
Destroyer Droid

Also known as droidekas, these killer droids curl up and roll like wheels until they reach their targets, when they uncurl, raise shields, and open fire.

ALIEN PROFILE
Toydarians

Toydarians are a winged species from the planet Toydaria. They are typically short with small trunks and tusks on their faces and bird-like legs that end in webbed feet. They can fly quite quickly, and prefer flight to walking.

Yoda

At nearly nine hundred years old, Yoda is without peer in his knowledge of the Force. He wields his lightsaber with blinding speed and uses his agility to render himself nearly invulnerable.

"Belief is not a matter of choice, but of conviction."

SYNOPSIS

In the Abregado system, Jedi Master Plo Koon's cruiser is attacked by General Grievous and the Separatists' secret new warship, the *Malevolence*. Anakin and Ahsoka set out, against the Council's wishes, to rescue Plo. Meanwhile, Plo and his clones are fighting for their lives in an escape pod as droid pod hunters slice their way through the debris. Arriving in the nick of time, Anakin and Ahsoka make the rescue and escape before the *Malevolence* can stop them – leaving Grievous to answer to Count Dooku.

VEHICLE PROFILE
Malevolence

Model: *Subjugator*-class heavy cruiser

Class: Heavy cruiser

Weapons:
- T2 ion pulse cannons
- Twin turbolaser batteries

Ahsoka Tano

Anakin Skywalker's young Padawan, Ahsoka Tano, is headstrong and independent . . . much like her Master.

EPISODE HIGHLIGHT

BOLDLY SPOKEN FOR ONE SO YOUNG.

SHE IS LEARNING FROM ANAKIN.

VEHICLE PROFILE
Jedi Cruiser

Model: *Venator*-class Star Destroyer

Class: Capital Ship

Weapons:
- Heavy turbolasers
- Torpedoes
- Fighter complement

NEWSREEL

The clone starfleet is under siege! Dozens of Republic warships have been destroyed in merciless surprise attacks that leave no survivors. Rumours spread of a terrible new Separatist weapon. In the face of growing fear, the Jedi Council sends Master Plo Koon to hunt down the menace before it strikes again . . . ■

KOH-TO-YA, LITTLE 'SOKA.

Plo Koon

Kel Dor Jedi Master from the planet of Dorin, Plo Koon is a skilled warrior and member of the Jedi High Council.

General Grievous

Commander of the
Separatist droid armies,
the ruthless cyborg
General Grievous is a
highly skilled warlord
with a personal vendetta
against the Jedi Order.

ALIEN PROFILE
Kel Dors

Sometimes referred to as Kel Dorians, this species
comes from the planet Dorin in the Expansion
Region. Because of the low oxygen atmosphere of
their homeworld, Kel Dors must wear protective
masks and goggles to shield them in oxygen-rich
atmospheres. They also have enlarged, external
sensory organs at the base of their skulls that
provide them with extrasensory abilities.

WEAPON PROFILE
Ion Cannon

Fires highly ionized particles that
interfere with the operation of
electronics and computer systems

VEHICLE PROFILE
Twilight

Model: G9 Rigger

Class: Freighter

Weapons:
- Three heavy blasters
- Rotating laser cannon with periscope control

EPISODE HIGHLIGHT

NOW THE REPUBLIC WILL LEARN OF OUR ION CANNON.

YOUR FAILURE IS MOST UNFORTUNATE.

I'LL NEED TO DISCUSS THIS WITH MY MASTER.

Clone Commander Wolffe

Wolffe is a veteran clone trooper commander serving on-board the *Venator*-class Star Destroyer *Triumphant* under Jedi General Plo Koon.

"Easy is the path to wisdom for those not blinded by themselves."

SYNOPSIS

General Grievous and the *Malevolence* make their way towards a Republic medical station. Anakin leads a squadron of Y-wing fighters to stop the battleship. He thinks that a team of small starfighters could outmanoeuvre the ship's ion cannon. Anakin leads the ship through a giant neebray-infested shortcut and beats Grievous to the station. The Y-wings attack the *Malevolence*'s ion cannon, causing it to backfire and disable the ship's hyperdrive.

Anakin Skywalker

As a General in the Grand Army of the Republic, Jedi Knight Anakin Skywalker commands the Star Destroyer *Resolute*.

MASTER SKYWALKER SEEMS TO INSPIRE GREAT CONFIDENCE IN HIS MEN.

HE DOES LEAD BY EXAMPLE.

ALIEN PROFILE
Kaminoans

Kaminoans are a highly intelligent species from the water-covered world of Kamino, which lies deep in the area known as Wild Space, far beyond the Outer Rim Territories. The Kaminoans are tall, thin beings with pale skin and small heads that sit atop long necks. Because of the Kaminoan's exceptional cloning technology, they were the perfect choice to create the Republic's clone army.

DOES ANYONE CARE WHAT THE PADAWAN THINKS?

Nala Se

Nala Se is a Kaminoan who works at Kaliida Shoals Medical Center and tends to injured clone troopers.

TARGET THOSE ESCAPE PODS, I HAVE A REPUTATION TO UPHOLD.

NEWSREEL

A deadly weapon unleashed! The Separatist battleship *Malevolence* advances unopposed through Republic space, tearing apart any ship that stands in its path. After a daring rescue and narrow escape, Anakin Skywalker prepares a counter-attack on the enemy and its diabolical droid commander, General Grievous . . . ∎

EPISODE HIGHLIGHT

TORPEDOES AWAY!

VEHICLE PROFILE

Plo Koon's Delta-7B *Aethersprite*-class light interceptor

Model: Delta-7B *Aethersprite*-class light interceptor

Class: Starfighter

Weapons:
- Laser cannons

R7-D4

Jedi Master Plo Koon's battle-worn astromech droid and copilot of his Delta-7B *Aethersprite*-class light interceptor.

TRIVIA

PLUNK PLUNK

These four-legged power droids are called plunk droids after the sound that they make.

ALIEN PROFILE
Neebrays

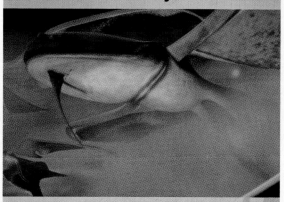

These great winged creatures are known in many parts of the galaxy, riding the solar winds along ancient migration routes in pods of adults and juveniles. They feed on the organic compounds within nebulae, and are generally found within these great clouds of gas and dust. But neebray have a complex lifecycle that xenobiologists are still studying. Newborn neebray, some no bigger than a human child's finger, are often found in the atmospheres of planets, where they feed on sunlight and atmospheric gases. Juveniles sometimes attach themselves to starships entering or leaving the atmosphere, but have also been found in deep space, apparently hibernating.

I CAN ALREADY TASTE IT.

Matchstick

Y-wing clone pilot in Shadow Squadron with the designation Shadow 2. He is one of several clone pilots to die in the Battle of the Kaliida Nebula.

IF ANYTHING, IT IS SKYWALKER WHO WILL UNDERESTIMATE THIS SHIP AND ITS POWER.

> "A plan is only as good as those who see it through."

SYNOPSIS

Republic cruisers continue to attack the damaged *Malevolence* as Senator Padmé Amidala's ship drops out of hyperdrive right next to the battleship. By the time she realizes that she's been tricked, her ship has been caught in the *Malevolence*'s tractor beam. Anakin and Obi-Wan head towards the *Malevolence* to rescue her. Once on-board the ship, they get separated and Obi-Wan battles Grievous as Anakin and Padmé sabotage the ship's navigation computer. The Jedi and Padmé escape the *Malevolence*, and Grievous chases after them in his starfighter. The *Malevolence* attempts to make the jump to hyperspace, but the coordinates that Anakin programs into the navigation computer send it crashing into a dead moon instead.

WE'RE DOOMED.

Senator Padmé Amidala

Padmé Amidala serves as the Senator of Naboo, taking the position once occupied by Palpatine. In a galaxy undergoing tumultuous changes, her outspoken nature has shone as a beacon of reason and rationality in an increasingly fragmented Senate.

B1 Battle Droid

The B1 battle droids serve as the main infantry of the Separatist Alliance. While they are not the most intelligent droids, they are unquestioningly loyal and fearless.

VEHICLE PROFILE
Soulless One

Class: Belbullab-22 starfighter

Weapons:
• Two triple laser cannons

DROID PROFILE
Protocol Droid

A droid whose primary purpose is to aid and assist diplomats and high-level figures. Their programming includes languages, cultures, and diplomacy. Common models are the TC and 3PO series. They were programmed with personalities, emotions, and the ability to learn and grow very similar to organic beings.

NEWSREEL

Grievous in retreat! Before the battleship *Malevolence* could destroy an Outer Rim clone medical base, a Republic strike force – under the command of Jedi General Anakin Skywalker – crippled the warship, disabling its dreaded ion cannon. Now the Jedi relentlessly pursue the *Malevolence . . .* ∎

EPISODE HIGHLIGHT

C-3PO

Senator Amidala's personal protocol droid. He is fluent in over six million forms of communication.

EPISODE HIGHLIGHT

GENERAL KENOBI, DID YOU REALLY THINK THAT I'D LEAVE THE HYPERDRIVE UNPROTECTED?

ANYTHING IS POSSIBLE . . .

YOU HAVEN'T EXACTLY IMPRESSED ME TODAY.

WEAPON PROFILE
ELG-3A Blaster Pistol

This compact blaster is standard issue on all Naboo royal cruisers and battleships.

TRIVIA

The Naboo yacht is an H-type Nubian yacht, which was created by the Nubian Design Collective, and then customized by the Theed Palace Space Vessel Engineering Corps for Senator Padmé Amidala's personal use.

> THERE HE GOES AGAIN, CRAVING ADVENTURE AND EXCITEMENT.

> YOU GET USED TO IT.

Admiral Wullf Yularen

Admiral in the Republic Navy under the command of Jedi General Anakin Skywalker, he serves aboard the Star Destroyer *Resolute*.

EPISODE HIGHLIGHT

> I DO BELIEVE I'M LOST IN ENEMY TERRITORY. AND ALL ALONE.

> DON'T SHOOT, I SURRENDER.

> R2-D2, OH MY, YOU ARE A SIGHT FOR SORE CIRCUITS.

> MASTER ANAKIN SENT YOU TO FIND ME? WHAT KEPT YOU THEN?

"The best confidence-builder is experience."

SYNOPSIS

Clone officers Commander Cody and Captain Rex are sent to inspect the remote Rishi outpost in the Outer Rim. The outpost is responsible for protecting the cloning facilities on Kamino. However, the outpost has been overrun with droid commandos, leaving only a handful of rookie clones left. Rex and Cody take command of these rookies and lead them on a daring mission to destroy the outpost and alert the Republic of the imminent attack on Kamino.

PROFILE
Clone Troopers

Identical soldiers created on the world of Kamino using the genetic template of Mandalorian bounty hunter Jango Fett.

Commander Cody

Commander of the the 212th Attack Battalion, Cody often serves alongside Jedi General Obi-Wan Kenobi.

LOOKS LIKE WE GOT OURSELVES A BATCH OF SHINIES.

EPISODE HIGHLIGHT

THEY SHOULD HAVE CHECKED IN FROM THE RISHI STATION HOURS AGO.

IT APPEARS YOUR CAPTAIN FOLLOWS ORDERS AS WELL AS YOU DO.

HMM. PERHAPS CODY IS BORING REX WITH STANDARD PROCEDURES AND PROTOCOL.

Commando Droids

Elite battle droids created for stealth assignments.

VEHICLE PROFILE

Obex

Model: *Nu*-class attack shuttle

Class: Shuttle

Weapons:
- Medium laser cannons
- Double light laser cannon

NEWSREEL

Clone forces rally! As the war escalates in the Outer Rim, the Jedi Knights are spread thinly across the galaxy. Many new clones are rushed into service to support their Jedi generals. Unfortunately, because of the relentless demands of battle, many young clones must join the struggle before their intensive training has been completed. These clones, manning a vital network of tracking stations, are all that stand between the Republic and invasion . . . ▉

> ROGER.
> ROGER.

WEAPON PROFILE
Thermal Detonator

A small, handheld explosive device

ALIEN PROFILE
Rishi Eels

A large, carnivorous moray-like creature native to the Rishi moon. It is capable of eating a person whole.

Hevy

A clone trooper assigned to the Rishi outpost, he has an affection for large weapons and valiantly sacrifices himself to save his fellow clones.

WEAPON PROFILE
DC-15A blaster rifle

A more powerful, long-ranging version of the DC-15S blaster.

Sergeant O-Niner

Commanding officer of the Rishi base, Sergeant O-Niner understands the importance of their assignment, and takes his responsibilities seriously.

WEAPON PROFILE
DC-17 Hand Blaster

A heavy blaster pistol used by clone captains and commanders.

"Trust in your friends, and they'll have reason to trust in you."

SYNOPSIS

Anakin executes a daring ambush on General Grievous's fleet, but suffers serious damage to his starfighter. When he wakes up in the medical bay, he's informed by Ahsoka that R2-D2 was lost in the battle. Obi-Wan Kenobi, concerned that R2-D2's memory contains Republic secrets, sends Anakin to find the droid. However, Anakin's new astromech droid, R3-S6, apparently malfunctions and almost delivers the Jedi into the waiting hands of Grievous.

YOU'LL BE SORRY YOU EVER CAME ABOARD MY SHIP, JEDI.

R2-D2

A spunky, independent astromech, R2-D2 serves Anakin Skywalker. His barrel-shaped body hides a huge number of tools, including a holoprojector and a computer interface.

VEHICLE PROFILE
V-19 Torrent starfighter

Model: V-19 Torrent starfighter

Class: Starfighter

Weapons:
- Blaster cannons
- Concussion missile launchers

ALIEN PROFILE
Trandoshans

Burly reptilians from the same star system as the Wookiees, Trandoshans are known for their great strength and ability to regenerate lost limbs. Many Trandoshans serve as bounty hunters or slavers.

Gha Nachkt

A Trandoshan scavenger who scours through the debris left in the aftermath of space battles during the Clone Wars in his freighter *Vulture's Claw*. An unscrupulous trader, he sells his salvage to the highest bidder.

EPISODE HIGHLIGHT

UGH. WHAT'S THAT SMELL?

YOU'LL GET USED TO IT.

NEWSREEL

After suffering a series of disastrous defeats at the hands of General Grievous, the Republic's foothold in the Outer Rim is in jeopardy. Commissioned to protect the strategic world of Bothawui, Anakin Skywalker and his weary battle group are all that stands between the system and domination by the droid army . . . ■

IG-86 Assassin Droid

Among the deadliest droids in the galaxy, the IG-86 droids are more intelligent and skilled than the standard B1 battle droids.

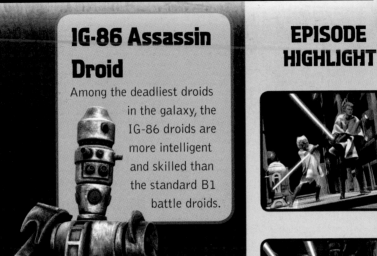

PLANET PROFILE
Bothawui

Region: Mid Rim

Bothawui is the home of the Bothans, master spies and information gatherers who are suspicious of other species and see politics as a ruthless game to be played with no let-up and no mercy.

LANGUAGE LESSONS

On the *Resolute*, Ahsoka's tactical readout says in Aurebesh: 4H50K4 RUL3Z TAKE THAT GRIEVOUS

VEHICLE PROFILE
Vulture's Claw

Model: GS-100 salvage ship

Class: Salvage ship

Weapons:

• Laser cannons

DROID PROFILE
Astromech Droids

Astromech droids are all-round utility droids that serve as automated mechanics, performing a variety of repair duties. Because astromechs can perform more than 10,000 operations per second, many serve aboard specially designed starfighters and provide additional navigation and copilot duties.

Medical Droid

A type of droid found throughout the galaxy, they are roughly humanoid-appearing droids with surgical appendages, medical diagnostic computers, and treatment analysis computers.

WEAPON PROFILE
E-5 Droid Blaster

A powerful, lightweight blaster rifle that is standard issue for all battle droids.

EPISODE HIGHLIGHT

SUICIDE IS NOT THE JEDI WAY, MASTER.

YOU SHOULD LISTEN TO YOUR PADAWAN.

AS YOU LISTENED TO YOURS, MY OLD MASTER?

"You hold on to friends by keeping your heart a little softer than your head."

SYNOPSIS

Anakin tracks a distress call from a captured R2-D2 to a secret Separatist listening post, Skytop Station. Aboard the station, Anakin sends Ahsoka and Rex to destroy the ship's reactors while he searches for his droid. Grievous ambushes Ahsoka and Rex, but the young Padawan engages the General, while Rex continues with the mission. Meanwhile, Anakin rescues R2-D2. They make it to the ship's hangar, only to learn that R3-S6 is a Separatist spy. Rex detonates the explosions and Grievous flees the station. R2-D2 defeats R3-S6 in battle and is rescued from the exploding station at the last minute by Anakin.

I WILL DEAL WITH THE JEDI MYSELF.

Trooper Denal

A veteran clone trooper under Rex's command, Denal finds himself forced to improvise after R3-S6's repeated failures during the Skytop Station mission.

NEWSREEL

Missing in action! Anakin Skywalker's heroic droid navigator R2-D2 was lost in battle. When a desperate search fails to locate R2, Anakin is forced to take on a new navigator, R3-S6. Now the Jedi embark on a dangerous new mission: to find a secret enemy listening post. Meanwhile, R2-D2 has fallen into the hands of a vile droid smuggler and is on his way to General Grievous, who will surely plunder the Republic's secrets hidden within him . . . ▮

Vulture Droid

These vicious mechanical killers are deadly on the ground and in space — they can walk on their wing-tips and then spring into the air to engage Republic starfighters.

VEHICLE PROFILE
P-38 Starfighter

Model: Porax-38 starfighter

Class: Starfighter

Weapons:
• Twin laser cannons

R3-S6

Nicknamed "Goldie" by Ahsoka Tano, R3-S6 had his programming sabotaged by Separatist agents, and is secretly reporting to General Grievous.

WEAPON PROFILE
Droid Popper

An electromagnetic pulse (EMP) grenade used to immobilize droids.

Model: Battlesphere

Class: Space station

MagnaGuard

These Separatist droids were built as bodyguards for General Grievous and mimic the look of Kaleesh warriors. Count Dooku has ordered more of them for his own use.

EPISODE HIGHLIGHT

GENERAL GRIEVOUS.

IT APPEARS THAT THIS MISSION MEMORY HAS NEVER BEEN ERASED.

IT CONTAINS EVERY REPUBLIC FORMATION AND STRATEGY THEY HAVE.

GOOD WORK. YOU HAVE CERTAINLY EARNED YOUR FEE THIS TIME.

MORE THAN MY FEE. THIS DROID IS WORTH MORE. I GET PAID MORE. NOW I SUGGEST . . .

HEH, HEH. THERE IS YOUR BONUS.

SYNOPSIS

Senator Padmé Amidala, Jar Jar Binks and C-3PO head to the planet of Rodia to meet with Senator Onaconda Farr. However, they are tricked into a Separatist ambush and Padmé is taken prisoner. Jar Jar, wearing a Jedi robe that he found on the ship, heads out to rescue her. Nute Gunray and his droid army believe Jar Jar to be a real Jedi and unleash their full force to stop him. Luckily, a swamp monster, who Jar Jar met in the water below the city, arrives just in time to stop Gunray and the droids.

Nute Gunray

The wicked Viceroy of the Trade Federation, Nute Gunray is a champion of the Separatist cause. He seeks revenge against Padmé Amidala for his defeat at Naboo.

HANG ON, THREE-SO!

IT'S THREEPIO.

DON'T SHOOT. WE SURRENDER.

Jar Jar Binks

A comically clumsy Gungan, Jar Jar Binks is seemingly always doing the wrong thing. Yet his friends also know that he's loyal, kind-hearted and means well.

ALIEN PROFILE
Gungans

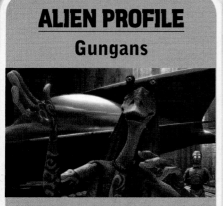

Gungans breathe both air and water, and are comfortable on land, though they are much more graceful under the sea. After millennia of mutual suspicion, they now live in peace with the human colonists of Naboo.

NEWSREEL

The Clone War threatens the unity of the Republic! As battles rage across the galaxy, more worlds succumb to the seductive lure of the Separatists and leave the Republic. On a vital mission of peace, Senator Padmé Amidala journeys to the Outer Rim world of Rodia, desperate to ensure its loyalty remains to the Republic . . . ∎

EPISODE HIGHLIGHT

Onaconda Farr

This Senator from Rodia has known Padmé since she was a little girl. With his people starving, he makes a desperate bargain with the Separatists.

ALIEN PROFILE
Rodians

A reptilian species, Rodians are loyal to their tight-knit clans. They are famous for their tracking skills, and some make their way in the galaxy as bounty hunters.

ALIEN PROFILE
Kwazel Maw

A feared predator of Rodia's seas, the Kwazel Maw is nearly 100 metres long. It generally lives in the depths, where it stuns prey with brilliant flashes of its bioluminescent markings.

EPISODE HIGHLIGHT

EPISODE HIGHLIGHT

POOR JAR JAR, HE WAS ALWAYS SUCH A MISFIT.

Silood

Onaconda Farr's long-time attendant, Silood is a quiet presence at the Senator's side, offering whispered advice when he thinks it appropriate.

CLOAK OF DARKNESS

"Ignore your instincts at your peril."

SYNOPSIS

Jedi Ahsoka Tano and Luminara Unduli have been tasked with escorting Nute Gunray back to Coruscant. Clone Commander Gree and a team of Senate commandos, under the command of Captain Argyus, have been sent to guard Gunray. However, a team of super battle droids, led by Asajj Ventress, board their ship. As the two Jedi try to fight off the assassin, Captain Argyus reveals himself as a traitor and frees Gunray — however, his treachery is repaid by Ventress's lightsaber in his back.

OPEN THIS DOOR AND I'LL BUY YOU A PLANET!

Commander Gree

Formally known as CC-1004, Gree is Luminara Unduli's second-in-command. A disciplined clone officer, he is baffled by the idea that a man like Argyus could betray the Republic that he serves.

NEWSREEL

Viceroy Gunray captured! Senator Padmé Amidala has scored a victory against the Separatist Alliance on the remote world of Rodia, securing the arrest of the diabolical Confederate leader, Nute Gunray. The Jedi Council has dispatched Master Luminara Unduli and Anakin Skywalker's Padawan, Ahsoka, to escort the Viceroy to Coruscant under heavy guard. Once there, he will face trial for his many war crimes . . . ∎

EPISODE HIGHLIGHT

TELL US WHAT WE WANT TO KNOW RIGHT NOW . . .

. . . OR I WILL GUT YOU LIKE A ROKARIAN DIRT-FISH!

ALIEN PROFILE
Neimoidians

As grubs, Neimoidians compete viciously for food, with the weak left to die. It's no wonder, then, that Neimoidians grow up to be intensely greedy beings who care little if others suffer.

VEHICLE PROFILE
Republic Frigate

Model: *Droch*-class boarding craft

Class: Boarding ship

Weapons:
• Crushing pincers

Luminara Unduli

A by-the-book Jedi from the planet Mirial, Luminara Unduli believes that Padawans should follow their Masters' orders without question, and that discipline will always win out over passion and rage.

EPISODE HIGHLIGHT

IF IT ISN'T THE HAIRLESS HARPY.

IF IT ISN'T SKYWALKER'S FILTHY, OBNOXIOUS LITTLE PET. STAND DOWN, LITTLE GIRL, AND I'LL GIVE YOU A COOKIE.

HOW NICE OF YOU. TELL YOU WHAT. I'LL GIVE YOU A MERCIFUL DEATH.

Captain Argyus

A Senate commando from a proud Core World family, Argyus has lost faith in the Republic and in himself, agreeing to betray the cause his family has served for generations for Separatist credits.

PROFILE
Senate Guards

These blue-armoured soldiers are one of Coruscant's proudest traditions, having protected the Senate for centuries. The best and bravest "Blue Guards" become commandos and are sent on secret Senate missions.

WHY'D YOU DO IT, ARGYUS?

A CLONE LIKE YOU WOULD NEVER UNDERSTAND. I WANTED A LIFE WITH MORE THAN EMPTY SERVITUDE.

AND, FOR THAT, YOU'D BETRAY THE REPUBLIC?

LIKE I TOLD THE PADAWAN: SOMETIMES BEING A GOOD SOLDIER MEANS DOING WHAT YOU THINK IS RIGHT.

YOU AND I DISAGREE ON WHAT MAKES A GOOD SOLDIER.

Darth Sidious

The secret leader of the Separatists, Darth Sidious is a shadowy Sith Lord who gives orders to Count Dooku. Sidious has a master plan for the Clone Wars which has yet to be revealed.

SOMETIMES I WONDER WHY YOU SUBMITTED TO THE CHANGES.

IMPROVEMENTS! I SUBMIT TO NO ONE. I CHOSE THEM! NOW GET ON WITH IT.

SYNOPSIS

Kit Fisto tracks Gunray to the moon of Vassek. There, he is met by his former Padawan, Nahdar Vebb, and a team of clone troopers. Gunray's location is revealed to be in a strange stone fortress. However, once inside, they realize they've been tricked by Count Dooku. Discovering that they're in General Grievous's lair, they plan a trap for him. But Grievous soon gets the upper hand and Nahdar finds himself alone and overpowered against Grievous. Trapped in Grievous's control room, Kit can only watch as his former Padawan is shot down.

Nahdar Vebb

A Mon Calamari Jedi who has just passed the trials and become a full Jedi Knight, Nahdar Vebb is impatient with the old Jedi traditions, which he thinks are of little use against the Separatist threat.

Kit Fisto

A Nautolan Jedi, Kit Fisto has a gentle manner and a quick laugh. But he's also one of the Jedi Order's fiercest fighters, as many an enemy of the Republic has discovered.

NEWSREEL

Viceroy Gunray escapes! En route to Coruscant to stand trial for war crimes, evil Separatist leader Nute Gunray has broken free of his Jedi escort. With the help of Count Dooku's sinister agents, the villainous Viceroy has made a daring getaway. Alerted to the bold prison break, Jedi Master Kit Fisto has traced the stolen ship to a remote system, hoping to recapture Gunray and return him to justice . . . ■

A4-D

The surgical droid, A4-D is responsible for keeping General Grievous in good health and good repair, and also serves as caretaker for the General's redoubt on Vassek.

EPISODE HIGHLIGHT

HOW QUICKLY POWER CAN CHANGE HANDS.

SURRENDER, AND I PROMISE YOU WILL DIE QUICKLY.

ALIEN PROFILE
Mon Calamari

The Mon Calamari hail from a planet near the edge of the galaxy, and are famous for being gifted starship designers and builders. Their homeworld has suffered terribly from Separatist attacks.

YOU EXPECT VICTORY OVER THE JEDI, BUT ALL YOU GIVE ME TO FIGHT THEM ARE BATTLE DROIDS! BAH!

ALIEN PROFILE
Roggwarts

Homeworld: Guiteica

Years before the Clone Wars, an army of Kaleesh and Jedi stormed the planet Guiteica, home to the Bitthævrian warriors. Many Kaleesh, including Grievous, took home baby roggwarts, training the creatures to be devoted pets and fierce watch-beasts.

EPISODE HIGHLIGHT

WHAT ABOUT YOUR FORMER PADAWAN?

HIS HEART WAS IN THE RIGHT PLACE, BUT HE TRIED TO ANSWER GRIEVOUS'S POWER WITH HIS OWN.

TO ANSWER POWER WITH POWER, THE JEDI WAY THIS IS NOT. IN THIS WAR, A DANGER THERE IS OF LOSING WHO WE ARE.

R6-H5

R6-H5 is Kit Fisto's astromech, and accompanies him to remote Vassek. Something of a worrywart, R6 is one of a number of Republic astromechs used for testing new prototype droid systems.

> "The winding path to peace is always a worthy one, regardless of how many turns it takes."

SYNOPSIS

Fleeing from an attempted ambush by Anakin Skywalker and Obi-Wan Kenobi, Count Dooku's ship crashes on the planet of Vanqor. Shortly after, Anakin and Obi-Wan's ship crashes in the same location. The two Jedi head into a cave to find Dooku, but he traps them in with an avalanche. He heads back to his ship to find it surrounded by pirates. Knowing that he's trapped, Dooku accepts their offer to fly him to a nearby planet. However, he arrives to find himself overpowered. The pirates wish to ransom him to the Republic, so Palpatine sends Anakin and Obi-Wan to confirm that they have Dooku. The two Jedi, however, find themselves captured by the pirates as well.

Count Dooku

The public leader of the Separatists, Count Dooku left the Jedi Order, dismayed at the corruption of the Republic, and now serves the Separatists' master.

ALIEN PROFILE
Weequays

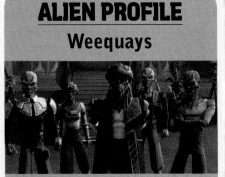

Weequays are leathery-skinned bipeds native to the desert planet Sriluur, near the central worlds controlled by the Hutts. They are frequently hired by Hutt crime lords as bodyguards or mercenaries, though they are not one of the giant slugs' slave species.

NEWSREEL

Manhunt! After a long and perilous search, the Jedi finally track down Separatist leader Count Dooku. During a heroic attempt to capture the Count, Anakin Skywalker has gone missing. Having lost contact with Skywalker, Obi-Wan Kenobi heads toward his friend's last known location – a lone Separatist frigate in the far reaches of the Outer Rim . . .

EPISODE HIGHLIGHT

HOW COME I'M THE ONE GETTING CAUGHT ALL THE TIME?

IT DOESN'T LOOK GOOD.

WHEN YOU'RE A JEDI MASTER, YOU CAN MAKE THE PLAN.

THAT'S JUST IT. HOW CAN I BECOME A JEDI MASTER IF I'M ALWAYS GETTING CAUGHT?

AT LEAST YOU'RE A MASTER AT GETTING CAUGHT.

Hondo Ohnaka

A Weequay pirate, Hondo Ohnaka and his gang prowl the galaxy's remote spacelanes, kidnapping travellers and holding them for ransom.

PLANET PROFILE
Vanqor

Region: Outer Rim

Inhabitants: Humans, gundarks

A desolate world far from the galaxy's population centres, Vanqor is known for its tough human inhabitants, as well as for the unfortunate number of gundark nests that dot its canyons, mountains, and badlands.

ALIEN PROFILE
Gundarks

Gundarks come in a variety of shapes and sizes and are found on different worlds, with some of the largest living on the desolate world of Vanqor. They are born with two arms and small ears, but later sprout additional arms and their ears grow dramatically.

VEHICLE PROFILE
Neimoidian Shuttle

Model: Sheathipede transport shuttle

Class: Shuttle

Weapons:
• Laser cannons

EPISODE HIGHLIGHT

I AM MORE POWERFUL THAN ANY JEDI.

KNOW THAT YOU ARE DEALING WITH A SITH LORD.

YOU'RE STILL OUTNUMBERED.

Pilf Mukmuk

A mischievous Kowakian monkey-lizard, Pilf Mukmuk is smarter than most people give him credit for, and helps capture Anakin and Obi-Wan.

Spacesuits

Spacesuits are used by individuals to enter space, often for the purpose of doing repairs on the surface or in the depressurized compartments of starships or space stations. However, during the Clone Wars, spacesuits are often used by the military.

I STILL DON'T GET IT.

GET WHAT?

HOW A BUNCH OF PIRATES MANAGED TO CATCH DOOKU WHEN WE COULDN'T.

MAYBE THERE'S A LESSON TO BE LEARNED HERE.

I STILL DON'T GET IT.

IT'S TO REMIND US TO BE HUMBLE . . .

AND NEVER TOO PROUD TO ACCEPT A GIFT WHEN IT COMES OUR WAY.

VEHICLE PROFILE
Solar Sailer

Model: Sloop

Class: Punworcca 116 Interstellar Sloop

Weapons:
- Tractor/repulsor beam array

"Fail with honour rather than succeed by fraud."

SYNOPSIS

After being drugged by Weequay pirates, Anakin and Obi-Wan wake to find themselves in a prison cell, tethered to Count Dooku. Meanwhile, the clones arrive with Dooku's ransom. Their shuttle is shot down by Hondo's rival Turk Falso, and Senator Kharrus is killed, leaving Jar Jar in charge. After several failed escape attempts, the Jedi are finally freed when Jar Jar accidentally knocks out the pirates' power supply. In the confusion, Dooku escapes.

DROID PROFILE
Pirate Guards

Normally, droids like this R5 unit are programmed never to harm living beings. But Hondo Ohnaka's pirates have hacked the logic modules of captured astromechs, turning them into armed sentries (with painted-on smiles).

Senator Kharrus

A three-eyed Gran, Kharrus is a veteran Senator used to the dangers of negotiations with the galaxy's more dangerous elements.

YOU WANT TO DEACTIVATE THE CELL BARS.

I . . . I . . . WANT TO . . .

YOU WANT TO DEACTIVATE THE CELL BARS AND GO OUT DRINKING.

I WANT TO DEACTIVATE THE CELL BARS AND GO OUT DRINKING!

Commander Stone

Formally known as CC-5869, Stone is a commander with the Coruscant Guard's Diplomatic Escort Group.

ALIEN PROFILE
Skalders

Barrel-chested grazers, skalders live on the plains of Florrum. They got their name from their habit of eating grass in the shadow of Florrum's geysers. But skalders can sense when a spume of superheated water is on the way, and their thick hides and great speed allow them to escape serious burns.

NEWSREEL

Dooku held for ransom! After escaping capture by Jedi Knights Anakin Skywalker and Obi-Wan Kenobi, the villainous Count Dooku fell into the clutches of pirates led by the brigand Hondo Ohnaka. Eager to get custody of Dooku, the Republic agreed to pay Hondo a hefty sum in exchange for the Sith Lord. But Anakin and Obi-Wan had not counted on the treacherous cunning of Ohnaka and his band . . . ∎

PLANET PROFILE
Florrum

Region: Outer Rim

Inhabitants: Skalders

A bleak planet located near Vanqor, Florrum isn't exactly a garden spot even by the low standards of the Outer Rim. But its proximity to a lawless trading route makes it the perfect location for a pirate lair.

VEHICLE PROFILE
Pirate Speeder Bike

Model: Starhawk speeder bike

Class: Speeder bike

Weapons:
• None

> YOU SHOULD BE MORE PATIENT, MASTER. AFTER ALL, THE COUNT IS AN ELDERLY GENTLEMAN AND DOESN'T MOVE LIKE HE USED TO.

> I SUPPOSE YOU'RE RIGHT.

Shuttle Pilot

Clones who have shown to have exceptional reflexes are trained by the Kaminoans to pilot a variety of Republic craft, from warships to shuttles and gunships.

JEDI! AFTER EVERYTHING, YOU'RE JUST GOING TO WALK AWAY?

WE HAVE NO QUARREL WITH YOU AND WE SEEK NO REVENGE.

INDEED. VERY HONOURABLE, MASTER JEDI.

OH, CAPTAIN, YOU WILL FIND THAT COUNT DOOKU DOES NOT SHARE OUR SENSE OF HONOUR . . . AND HE KNOWS WHERE YOU LIVE.

Turk Falso

Hondo's lieutenant, the Weequay Turk Falso, decides to betray his boss in hopes of taking over the leadership of the Ohnaka Gang.

VEHICLE PROFILE
Pirate Tank

Model: Ubrikkian Ord Pedrovia WLO-5 speeder tank

Class: Speeder

Weapons:
- Heavy laser cannon
- Antipersonnel laser cannons

"Greed and fear of loss are the roots that lead to the tree of evil."

SYNOPSIS

Anakin is severely injured rescuing Aayla Secura from an attack on her Star Destroyer. During their escape, their frigate is damaged and crashes on the remote world of Maridun. Ahsoka is worried about her Master and seeks help from the local Lurmen, who are peaceful and reject the Jedi and clones. Their leader, Tee Watt Kaa, eventually allows his son, Wag Too – who is a healer – to help Anakin.

LANGUAGE LESSONS

As the Jedi cruiser speeds towards Maridun the Twi'lek in the cockpit reads off

Commander Bly

Bly, formally known as CC-5052, serves Aayla Secura and is intensely loyal to her, though suspicious of how reckless other Jedi generals can be.

NEWSREEL

The Republic fleet is on the defensive and pushed to the brink! As war rages in the much contested Outer Rim Territories, chaos and fear mount as the Separatist army wages an epic battle against heavily outnumbered Republic ships in the far reaches of the Quell system. Anakin Skywalker and his Padawan, Ahsoka, race across the galaxy to aid Jedi Knight Aayla Secura, who is in the midst of a fight for her life as the sinister droid army closes in . . . ■

EPISODE HIGHLIGHT

I CAN'T LEAVE HIM! MASTER, I KNOW IF I WAS HURT, HE'D NEVER LEAVE ME BEHIND!

I KNOW THIS IS HARD, AHSOKA.

BUT ANAKIN HAS TO STAY BEHIND AND WE HAVE TO GO NOW. THERE'S NOTHING MORE WE CAN DO FOR HIM.

Aayla Secura

Twi'lek Jedi Aayla Secura's agility and athleticism make her one of the Jedi Order's deadliest fighters. She is also a mentor to young Jedi such as Ahsoka Tano.

ALIEN PROFILE
Lurmen

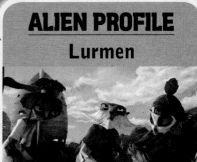

The Lurmen are native to Mygeeto, a planet controlled by the Separatist Banking Clan. They are both speedy and smart, combining lightning-quick reflexes with superb eyesight, hearing, and a sense of smell. Those keen senses are needed to survive on a world as hostile as Maridun.

Tee Watt Kaa

An elder of the Lurmen's Te Padka faith, Tee Watt Kaa is a devout pacifist who has led his followers across the galaxy to Maridun in an effort to escape the Clone Wars.

ALIEN PROFILE
Mastiff Phalones

The giant, vicious avians known as mastiff phalones are native to Maridun, where they prowl the grasslands in packs. They are descended from flying creatures, but evolution long ago turned their wings into powerful limbs tipped with terrible claws.

PLANET PROFILE
Quell

Region: Outer Rim

Inhabitants: Various

The deep blue world of Quell is one of many remote worlds with the poor luck to become a battleground between Separatist and Republic forces, who duel high in the planet's skies.

EPISODE HIGHLIGHT

HEY, KID!

I KNOW! I KNOW! I'M HANGING ON!

DROID PROFILE
Rocket Super Battle Droid

Super battle droids are tough but frustratingly slow for Separatist commanders who want to throw them at Republic forces. The B2-RP battle droid is designed to address this weakness, allowing the droids to fly to the fight and engage the enemy.

Tactical Droid

In an effort to turn the tide of the war, the Separatists have begun deploying tactical droids to lead units into battle. Tactical droids are emotionless, collecting relevant data about enemy units, and computing odds to determine the ideal strategy for the battlefield.

EPISODE HIGHLIGHT

GENERAL? ARE YOU ALL RIGHT?

BE . . . BE . . . HIND . . . YOU . . .

SYNOPSIS

As Anakin is healing, Rex spots a Separatist ship heading towards the planet. Separatist general Lok Durd announces that the village is under protection from the Separatists – and then orders the droids to ransack it. Durd has a weapon – the defoliator capsule – which is designed to destroy only organic matter, but leave machinery unharmed. The Jedi convince the Lurmen to fight for their home and, together, they stop Durd and destroy the defoliator.

EPISODE HIGHLIGHT

WHY ARE THEY TEARING APART OUR HOMES? WE'VE DONE NOTHING TO THEM!

VIOLENCE. THAT'S WHAT THOSE DROIDS ARE PROGRAMMED FOR.

Pune Zingat

Lok Durd's chief weapons technician is Pune Zingat, an Aqualish, whose careful planning and design work have much to do with the Neimoidian's success.

DROID PROFILE
Recon Droid

Hovering recon droids come in a number of shapes and sizes, and are programmed to sneak behind enemy lines and use their finely-honed sensors to spy on Republic officers' conversations.

NEWSREEL

Republic forces in retreat! While rescuing General Aayla Secura from certain defeat, Anakin Skywalker has been seriously injured. After a narrow escape, our heroes crash-landed on the remote world of Maridun. Stranded, and with no way to contact the Republic, the Jedi receive medical aid from the peaceful Lurmen colonists. But even on this tiny planet, the war threatens to follow the Jedi . . . ■

WEAPON PROFILE
Defoliator

Lok Durd's latest invention is the defoliator capsule, a missile that kills all living matter within its blast radius but leaves machinery – such as battle droids – intact.

EPISODE HIGHLIGHT

UH, SHOULD WE TAKE COVER?

NO, IDIOT. IT'S NOT EVEN GOING TO HIT US.

Lok Durd

An arrogant Neimoidian weapons researcher, Lok Durd is cruel and ambitious. He thinks nothing of testing his latest weapon on a peaceful Lurmen colony, hoping success will send him higher up the Separatist chain of command.

ALIEN PROFILE
Aqualish

The Aqualish have long resisted Republic authority, launching numerous uprisings in their galactic neighbourhood. During the Clone Wars, their planet secedes from the galaxy and supports the Separatist cause.

DROID PROFILE
Super Battle Droid

B2 battle droids are big, tough and dumb – and so aggressive they sometimes shove other Separatist droids out of the way as they stomp into combat.

Wag Too

A young Lurmen healer, Wag Too is the son of Tee Watt Kaa and was groomed by his father to lead the Maridun colony.

EPISODE HIGHLIGHT

Tub

A young Lurmen and friend of Wag Too's, Tub is one of the colony's best scouts. He is able to move through Maridun's grasslands speedily and silently.

ALIEN PROFILE
Carrier Butterflies

Beautiful, brightly coloured carrier butterflies are one of the few lifeforms on Maridun that won't try to bite or claw you to death. Carrier butterflies are surprisingly intelligent: the Lurmen raise them from pupae and have taught them to convey simple messages.

LANGUAGE LESSONS

The Aurebesh writing on the side of the shield generators that the Jedi and clones steal from the Separatists reads: CAUTION.

"Arrogance diminishes wisdom."

SYNOPSIS

Republic gunships arrive on the ice-covered planet of Orto Plutonia to find an empty base and a row of clone helmets on pikes. Pantorian Chairman Cho, whose moon controls this world, blames the Separatists and believes that they are building a secret base to attack Pantora. Obi-Wan and Anakin come across the Talz village. Cho tells the Talz leader, Thi-Sen, that he will not leave Orto Plutonia and declares war on the Talz. Cho is wounded before Senator Chuchi is given the authority to negotiate peace with the Talz.

> LISTEN HERE, YOU SAVAGE: THIS WORLD BELONGS TO THE MOON OF PANTORA.

Senator Chuchi

Young Riyo Chuchi disagrees with Chairman Cho's hostility and inflexibility, but can't think of a way to overrule her fellow Pantoran and avert a war with the Talz.

NEWSREEL

Republic outpost, overrun! The Jedi have lost all contact with the clone security force stationed on the bleak, snow-covered planet of Orto Plutonia. Obi-Wan Kenobi and Anakin Skywalker, accompanied by dignitaries from the nearby moon of Pantora, are sent to investigate the disappearance of the clone troopers on the desolate and forbidding landscape . . . ■

EPISODE HIGHLIGHT

Chairman Cho

Chi Cho has zealously defended Pantora for decades, and now sees anyone who disagrees with him as an enemy of his beloved people.

PLANET PROFILE
Orto Plutonia

Region: Outer Rim

Inhabitants: Talz

The Pantorans have declared that the frozen world of Orto Plutonia is their property. But for their claim to be accepted under Republic law, Orto Plutonia must be devoid of intelligent native life – and the Talz seem to have been there for many years.

VEHICLE PROFILE
Freeco Bikes

Model: CK-6 Swoop

Class: Speeder bike

Weapons:
• Laser cannons

TRESPASS

Episode 15

ALIEN PROFILE
Pantorans

Blue-skinned near-humans, Pantorans are believed to be an offshoot of the Inner Rim's Wroonians. They fear their remote world will be the next target of the Separatist military machine.

EPISODE HIGHLIGHT

NOW THAT YOU HAVE CREATED PEACE BETWEEN YOUR PEOPLE AND THE TALZ . . .

REMEMBER ONE CRUCIAL THING.

YES, MASTER KENOBI?

MAKE IT LAST, SENATOR. MAKE IT LAST.

Snow Gear
On Orto Plutonia, the clone troopers under Rex's command must wear rebreather hoods and thick thermal suits for protection from the bone-chilling cold. While necessary for survival, the extra gear restricts their movements in battle.

Thi-Sen

The Talz chieftain, Thi-Sen, known as the "Son of the Suns", was born amid omens of greatness and must prove himself by defending his people against new invaders.

ALIEN PROFILE
Talz

White-furred, four-eyed bipeds with sharp claws, the Talz are technologically primitive but cunning warriors. They are native to Alzoc III, but a colony has lived on frigid Orto Plutonia for thousands of years.

"Truth enlightens the mind and will always bring happiness to your side."

I REALLY WISH YOU HADN'T NOTICED THAT, SIR.

SYNOPSIS

Building up to the events in the movie, Anakin and Obi-Wan realize that someone has been giving their plans to the Separatists when an ambush goes wrong and their secret location is swarmed by battle droids. As the Jedi investigate a Separatist base and are confronted by Ventress, Cody and Rex learn that the spy is one of their clones, Sergeant Slick.

EPISODE HIGHLIGHT

Chopper

The clone nicknamed Chopper is a bit strange. He takes battle-droid fingers as war trophies. That's against the rules, but does it make him a traitor?

PROFILE
501st Legion

An elite unit of clone troopers led by Captain Rex, under the command of Jedi General Anakin Skywalker.

Sergeant Slick

The veteran clone officer Sergeant Slick is actually a Separatist agent, infuriated at what he sees as the enslavement of his fellow clones by the Republic.

NEWSREEL

A planet under siege! Separatist forces mercilessly batter the beautiful and elegant world of Christophsis. Unable to defend themselves any longer, the people of Christophsis call upon the Jedi for assistance. Hoping to save lives and prevent further destruction, Obi-Wan Kenobi and Anakin Skywalker plan a daring ambush that can turn the tide in the fight for this crucial star system . . . ▮

VEHICLE PROFILE
Single Trooper Aerial Platform

Model: Starhawk speeder bike

Class: Airspeeder

Weapons:
• Blaster cannons

VEHICLE PROFILE

BARC Speeder

Model: Biker Advanced Recon Commando speeder

Class: Speeder bike

Weapons:
• Laser cannons

Punch and Sketch

As clones in Slick's platoon, Punch and Sketch are suspected of being Separatist agents. But the two have a good alibi — they were in the base's mess hall.

Whorm Loathsom

A general from the planet Kerkoidia, the ruthless Whorm Loathsom has won the respect of Coruscant's strategists for his repeated victories over Republic forces.

LANGUAGE LESSONS

Clone Trooper Sketch's tattoo is an Aurebesh 'S'.

"Fear is a disease; hope is its only cure."

SYNOPSIS

Padmé and Jar Jar are captured by evil scientist Dr Nuvo Vindi after uncovering a secret lab developing the Blue Shadow Virus. Anakin and Ahsoka are sent to Naboo to stop Vindi before he can release the virus, which, if he succeeds, could lead to a galaxy-wide plague. Clone troopers, led by Rex, swarm the lab and deactivate the virus bombs, while Anakin captures a fleeing Vindi.

WONDERFUL SPECIMENS!

ALIEN PROFILE
Shaaks

Naboo's humans and Gungans both prize these fat, dim herd beasts for their meat. Though stupid and often sluggish, shaaks' gentle natures are appreciated by their handlers.

Peppi Bow

A shaak herder from Naboo's swamplands, Peppi Bow is determined to discover the source of the waterborne disease that killed her animals.

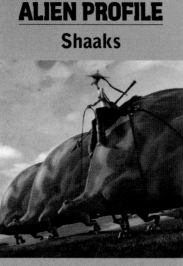

NEWSREEL

Battle droids on Naboo! As the Separatist rebellion rages through the galaxy, even peaceful planets are threatened. Following the discovery of Separatist droids wandering the grassy wasteland, Naboo is once again on high alert. Fearing their home is facing another invasion, Senator Amidala and Representative Binks race to Naboo to assess the situation. Meanwhile, near the Gungan swamplands, an even graver threat is about to be discovered . . . ▮

EPISODE HIGHLIGHT

THERE'S A GOOD CHANCE WE'RE ABOUT TO DESTROY ALL LIFE ON THIS PLANET, INCLUDING THE SENATOR'S.

SO, YES. I'M ON EDGE. WHY AREN'T YOU?

I'M BETTER AT HIDING IT.

LEP-86C8

A Coachelle Automata servant droid, 86C8 seems like most LEP droids — little more than a cute plaything. But this little droid has a deadly toy.

ALIEN PROFILE
Slug-Beetles

These bright blue insects dwell along the roots of the perlote trees found in Naboo's swamps. They are prized as delicacies by Gungans, who often go to considerable lengths to catch so tasty a snack.

VEHICLE PROFILE
Naboo Scout Carrier

Model: Theed Hangars Scout Carrier

Class: Scout ship

Weapons:
• Laser cannons

Dr Nuvo Vindi

Nuvo Vindi is as brilliant as he is dangerous – he loves the purity of viruses, and dreams of a galaxy ruled by viruses after all "higher" life has been destroyed.

PROFILE
Blue Shadow Virus

A generation before the Clone Wars, a quarantine contained the Candorian plagues, and the Blue Shadow Virus responsible was eliminated from the galaxy. Or so scientists thought. Now, Dr Vindi has brought the virus back and engineered it to be deadlier than ever.

PLANET PROFILE
Naboo

Ten years before the Clone Wars, Naboo was invaded by the Trade Federation. The efforts of a band of heroes including Padmé Amidala, Jar Jar Binks, Anakin Skywalker and Obi-Wan Kenobi wrecked Nute Gunray's plans – and the Trade Federation Viceroy swore one day he would have his revenge.

EPISODE HIGHLIGHT

Naboo Guardsman

The Royal Naboo Security Forces are charged with the defence of Naboo as well as serving as bodyguards for the ruling monarch and their court.

JEDI OR NOT, NOBODY GETS OFF THIS ROCK ALIVE.

SYNOPSIS

The clones realize that one of the vials of the Blue Shadow Virus is missing from Vindi's lab. Before they can contain the last vial, Padmé, Jar Jar, Ahsoka and Rex are all poisoned. Anakin and Obi-Wan head to the planet Iego to find the only known cure. However, Iego has problems of its own — it's surrounded by a network of laser stations programmed to shoot down any starship that tries to leave.

ALIEN PROFILE
Xandu

Leathery-winged predators, xandu glide among Iego's peaks, hunting for unwary creatures they can snatch from cliffs and ledges.

Captain Gregar Typho

A one-eyed veteran of the invasion of Naboo, Typho has sworn to protect Padmé Amidala against the next Separatist plot aimed at her.

PLANET PROFILE
Iego

Region: Outer Rim

Most think Iego is a legend, the cursed home of angels and marooned space pilots. As Obi-Wan and Anakin discover, these stories are true, from a certain point of view.

LANGUAGE LESSONS

The city of Cliffhold is full of Aurebesh graffiti. Look around and you'll find Jaybo Hood's name on several surfaces.

Amit Noloff

Once a successful spice merchant, the Quarren Amit Noloff has gone mad while marooned on Iego, and now tells all who will listen about the Curse of Drol.

EPISODE HIGHLIGHT

WHERE'S THE ANTIDOTE, VINDI?

HEHEHE. YOU MISTAKE MY ROLE, JEDI.

MY JOB WAS TO MANUFACTURE THE PLAGUE, NOT TO CURE IT.

NEWSREEL

Hard-pressed Jedi and their valiant clone troopers have thwarted an insidious Separatist plot to plant bombs loaded with the deadly Blue Shadow Virus in key Republic systems. Obi-Wan Kenobi and Anakin Skywalker have captured the vile scientist behind the nefarious scheme: Dr Nuvo Vindi. Now the Jedi plan to transport Vindi to the Republic capital for trial . . . ■

ALIEN PROFILE
Quarren

The Quarren have been rivals and occasional antagonists of the Mon Calamari for millennia, and some of their best starship engineers have pledged their loyalty and expertise to the Separatist cause.

WEAPON PROFILE
Drol

The ghost that imprisons Iego's population is actually a network of laser stations programmed to shoot down starships—a remnant of the days when the Separatists used Iego as a base.

The Angels

Formally known as the Diathim, Iego's Angels are reputed to be the most beautiful creatures in the galaxy. Anakin Skywalker heard of them when he was a child on Tatooine — but never imagined they were real.

Jaybo Hood

A young Iegan with a gift for tinkering with droids, Jaybo Hood has made himself into a little despot served by reprogrammed Separatist droids.

EPISODE HIGHLIGHT

ALIEN PROFILE
Reeksa Vines

Iego's reeksa vines stretch from the dim bottoms of canyons to the sunny tops of the planet's crags. But travellers are warned not to touch them, for fear of a close encounter with the plants' razor-sharp thorns and snapping jaws.

"It is a rough road that leads to the heights of greatness."

DID YOU TRAIN HER NOT TO FOLLOW ORDERS?

SYNOPSIS

Anakin and Ahsoka must destroy the Separatist blockade around the planet of Ryloth so Obi-Wan can get his landing party to the planet's surface. Outgunned, Anakin devises a plan. Pretending that he is ready to surrender, the Jedi crashes an empty Star Destroyer into the Separatist battleship while Ahsoka leads the starfighters to finish the job.

ALIEN PROFILE
Twi'leks

Twi'leks are graceful humanoids famous for their long brain-tails, known as lekku. They have been part of galactic society for millennia, but face extermination at the hands of the Separatists.

Clone Pilot Axe

A capable clone trooper pilot, Axe normally served as Blue Leader, but hands his squadron over to Ahsoka Tano for the attempt to break the Ryloth blockade.

NEWSREEL

Planet Ryloth invaded! Subjected to a brutal droid occupation, the people of Ryloth are starving under the blockade of a Separatist fleet. Evil Separatist leader Wat Tambor now rules with an iron fist. Answering a plea from the Senate, the Grand Army of the Republic mounts a bold offensive to liberate the system. It is up to Anakin Skywalker and his Padawan Ahsoka to make way for Obi-Wan's ground assault . . . ∎

Clone Pilot Kickback

As a member of Blue Squadron, clone pilot Kickback serves under Ahsoka Tano as Blue Four while attempting to liberate Ryloth from the Separatists.

VEHICLE PROFILE

Trade Federation Battleship

Model: Modified *Lucrehulk* Cargo Freighter

Class: Capital ship

Weapons:
- Turbolasers, starfighter complement

EPISODE HIGHLIGHT

THIS IS MY FIRST TIME COMMANDING A SQUADRON, R7. LET'S MAKE A GOOD IMPRESSION.

WEET TOO WEET

OK, YOU BOYS READY?

THIS IS TWO, AXE, READY WHEN YOU ARE, SKIPPER.

PLANET PROFILE
Ryloth

Region: Outer Rim

Ryloth has long been a source of slaves and spice, with Twi'leks sometimes decrying these cruel trades but just as often profiting from them. Ryloth's strategic location and great wealth make it a Separatist target.

VEHICLE PROFILE
Escape Pod

Model: *Venator*-class Star Destroyer escape pod

Class: Lifeboat

Weapons:
- None

Mar Tuuk

A capable Neimoidian officer, Mar Tuuk oversees the Separatists' Ryloth blockade. He correctly predicts that Anakin Skywalker will return to the battle — but not how the Jedi will do so.

EPISODE HIGHLIGHT

SKYWALKER, WHAT TREACHERY IS THIS? YOU HAVE NOTHING TO BARGAIN WITH!

IN THAT CASE, I'LL BE GOING . . . OH, YOU CAN STILL HAVE MY SHIP.

EPISODE HIGHLIGHT

IT WASN'T YOUR FAULT.

I LOST SO MANY OF MY PILOTS.

TAKE HEART, LITTLE ONE, THAT'S THE REALITY OF COMMAND.

R7-A7

R7-A7 serves as Ahsoka Tano's astromech during the strike on the Ryloth blockade. The droid is one of several in the Republic fleet with advanced prototype logical modules.

"The costs of war can never be truly accounted for."

NERRA. NERRA.

SYNOPSIS

On the surface of Ryloth, Obi-Wan and Rex lead a small attack force to destroy Separatist proton cannons that are being protected by a shield of captive Twi'leks. Troopers Waxer and Boil find a small Twi'lek girl named Numa who leads them through a secret passage to the prisoners. Once the Twi'leks are free, Obi-Wan and the clones are able to destroy the proton cannons, allowing Mace Windu's invasion force to arrive.

Waxer

Waxer, along with clone trooper Boil, serves under Commander Cody in the 212th Attack Battalion. They are sent to search a Twi'lek village for Separatist units.

I CALCULATE THE REMAINING CLONES ARE ATTEMPTING A DESPERATE FINAL OFFENSIVE.

NEWSREEL

Invasion! Separatist leader Wat Tambor has taken control of the planet Ryloth and subjugated its people through a brutal droid occupation. In a daring surprise attack, Jedi Anakin Skywalker and his Padawan, Ahsoka Tano, defeated the space blockade guarding the planet. Now, Jedi generals Mace Windu and Obi-Wan Kenobi lead a massive invasion to liberate the starving people . . . ∎

THEIR CHANCES OF SUCCESS AGAINST US ARE 742 TO 1.

YOU HAD BETTER BE RIGHT.

EPISODE HIGHLIGHT

I AM A DROID. I AM ALWAYS RIGHT.

Boil

Along with clone trooper Waxer, Boil serves under Commander Cody in the 212th Attack Battalion. They are sent to search a Twi'lek village for Separatist units.

ALIEN PROFILE
Gutkurrs

Gutkurrs are fierce predators who use their insect-like claws to dig themselves into Ryloth's desert sands, where they ride out heat storms and wait for prey to ambush.

WEAPON PROFILE
Proton Cannon

These artillery units can fire projectiles high into the atmosphere. They can be controlled by a gunner or fighter using their own built-in droid brains.

Numa

A young Twi'lek, Numa has escaped capture by battle droids thanks to her ability to move quickly and quietly and her knowledge of the tunnels beneath her village.

HIGHLIGHT

LESSON

One of the green lights on
TX-20's head indicates that it
COMIC RELIEF

Mace Windu

A tough, no-nonsense member
of the Jedi Council, Mace
Windu is a terrible opponent
for all those who would oppose
the dictates of the Jedi Order.

LIBERTY ON RYLOTH

Episode 2

> "Compromise is a virtue to be cultivated,
> not a weakness to be despised."

YOU DON'T SURVIVE
IN THE OUTER RIM BY
BEING STUPID!

SYNOPSIS

To defeat the Separatists on Ryloth and free the
Twi'leks, Mace Windu enlists the aid of freedom fighter
Cham Syndulla. With bombers destroying the Twi'lek
villages, Windu leads his invasion team to the heavily
protected Separatist headquarters. As Wat Tambor
prepares to escape, the Republic and freedom fighters
storm the base and bring an end to the occupation.

Wat Tambor

The Skakoan foreman of the Techno
Union, Wat Tambor is named emir
of occupied Ryloth, which he seeks
to strip of its valuables.

ALIEN PROFILE
Skakoans

Skakoans evolved in a highly pressured
methane atmosphere. When away from their
home planet, they must wear protective suits
and special breathing equipment.

NEWSREEL

Republic victory is at hand! Clone troopers under the command of the Jedi have successfully invaded the Separatist-occupied world of Ryloth. Anakin Skywalker battles the enemy in the skies, while Obi-Wan Kenobi frees villages from the grip of vile Separatist leader Wat Tambor. Now Jedi General Mace Windu leads the attack on the enemy lines in the final offensive to liberate the capital city of Lessu . . . ∎

LANGUAGE LESSONS

The back of Clone Commander Ponds's helmet says: SOME GUYS HAVE ALL THE LUCK in Aurebesh.

Commander Ponds

Formally known as CC-6454, Clone Commander Ponds serves Mace Windu, and regrets that service to the Jedi normally leaves him stuck on Coruscant, far from the front lines.

EPISODE HIGHLIGHT

VEHICLE PROFILE
Hyena Bomber

Model: Baktoid Self-Propelled heavy ordinance battle droid

Class: Bomber

Weapons:
• Laser cannons, concussion missiles

LIBERTY ON RYLOTH

Episode 21

Orn Free Taa

A Twi'lek Senator, the hopelessly corrupt Orn Free Taa spends most of his time on Coruscant, far from his ravaged homeworld.

VEHICLE PROFILE
AT-RT

Model: All Terrain Recon Transport

Class: Walker

Weapons:
• Laser cannons

EPISODE HIGHLIGHT

GENERAL WINDU! PERHAPS WE CAN COME TO A COMPROMISE.

NOT WHEN I HOLD ALL THE CARDS.

TRIVIA

Look fast and you'll see battle droids carrying off the Ark of the Convenant as part of Wat Tambor's stolen stash. Will it be crated up in a warehouse somewhere on Skako?

Cham Syndulla

A Twi'lek revolutionary, Cham Syndulla has long opposed Ryloth's leadership. Now he leads the freedom fighters trying to defeat the occupying Separatists.

THE REPUBLIC WILL HELP YOU REBUILD. WE WON'T ABANDON YOU.

YOUR TROOPS WILL STAY FOR SECURITY?

FOR A WHILE. TO KEEP THE PEACE.

ANOTHER ARMED OCCUPATION IS NOT A FREE RYLOTH.

HOW LONG BEFORE I AM FIGHTING YOU, MASTER JEDI?

ALIEN PROFILE
Blurrgs

Two-legged reptilian beasts, blurrgs are found on a number of worlds, from Endor to Ryloth. Twi'leks are skilled blurrg handlers, and ride the creatures into battle against the Separatists' droid armies.

"A secret shared is a trust formed."

SYNOPSIS

Trapped without his lightsaber, Anakin tries to stop bounty hunter Cad Bane and his band of criminals from seizing control of the Senate building. With Padmé and the other Senators held hostage, Bane demands that Palpatine release Ziro the Hutt from prison. Although Anakin is able to free the captured Senators, he is too late to prevent Cad Bane from getting away with Ziro.

TIME TO PAY UP, HUTT. I DON'T WORK FOR FREE.

Aurra Sing

A bounty hunter with long limbs and bone-white skin, the pitiless Aurra Sing is known as a crack shot with a blaster rifle.

NEWSREEL

Danger looms! Despite recent victories in the Outer Rim, criminal minds plot at the very heart of the Republic! The bounty hunter Cad Bane has assembled some of the deadliest criminals in the galaxy and plans a daring attack to seize members of the Senate. What can be the aim of this despicable act . . . ?■

Cad Bane

A deadly Duros bounty hunter, Cad Bane is known for always getting his prey — and for being willing to take on any assignment that pays him enough credits.

WEAPON PROFILE
Czerka Adventurer

This long-barrelled weapon can fire a variety of ammunition at targets thousands of metres away – but its wielder must have a remarkably steady hand.

EPISODE HIGHLIGHT

PUT UP YOUR HANDS.

I GOT BUSINESS WITH THE SENATE.

HOW 'BOUT YOU FELLAS STEP ASIDE?

ON YOUR KNEES AND RAISE YOUR HANDS! SLOWLY!

SON, I WOULDN'T BE SO HASTY IF I WERE YOU.

DROID PROFILE
Betty Droid

BD-3000s are programmed to look and act like young females, and were fashionable on Coruscant during the Clone Wars. They serve Senators and Coruscant's super-rich as attendants.

WEAPON PROFILE
Customized LL-30 Blaster Pistol

Used by bounty hunter Cad Bane, the LL-30 blaster pistols have a unique sound when fired and are equipped with a sight along the barrel.

Robonino

A pint-sized member of Cad Bane's crew of hunters, Robonino is a skilled slicer who moves quickly to shut down the power in the Senate complex.

EPISODE HIGHLIGHT

EPISODE HIGHLIGHT

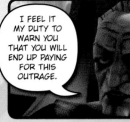

I FEEL IT MY DUTY TO WARN YOU THAT YOU WILL END UP PAYING FOR THIS OUTRAGE.

I CAN LIVE WITH THAT.

Ziro the Hutt

Also a crime lord of the Desilijic family, Jabba's flamboyant but equally dangerous uncle keeps his business centred in Coruscant, rather than the traditional Hutt Space.

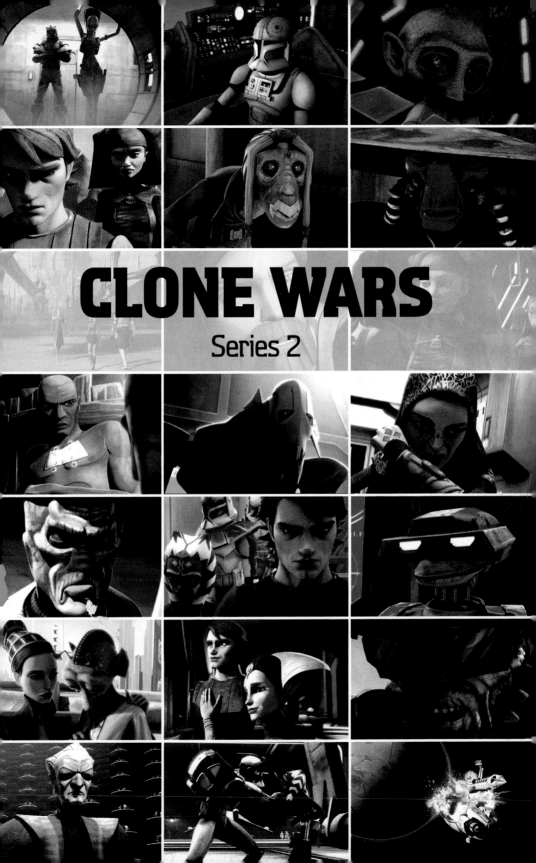

CLONE WARS

Series 2

"A lesson learned is a lesson earned."

SYNOPSIS

Ahsoka is sent to help in the Jedi library as punishment for ignoring orders during battle. This should be a quiet assignment, but Cad Bane and his droid Todo 360 have infiltrated the Jedi Temple to steal a holocron from the library vault. Helping them is Cato Parasitti, a changeling disguised as the Jedi Ord Enisence. Ahsoka discovers Parasitti's ruse and defeats her in a lightsaber duel. But while the Jedi are catching Cato and Todo, Bane sneaks away with the holocron.

> OUR WAR OPERATIONS, IT WAS NEVER ABOUT.

Cato Parasitti

A Clawdite spy and assassin, Cato Parasitti accepts Cad Bane's offer to infiltrate the Jedi library disguised as Ord Enisence. She can't resist the idea of walking undetected amid Jedi.

LANGUAGE LESSON

The display on the bomb panel inside Todo 360 is one of: COUNTDOWN TO DEATH

NEWSREEL

Jedi trapped on Felucia! Clones are surrounded by droid forces. Their only hope is to escape on Republic gunships waiting to land on the embattled surface. Jedi cruisers have managed to blow a hole in the droid defences, and have sent gunships to the rescue . . . ▪

Todo 360

A worrywart techno-service droid, Todo 360 wants nothing to do with the dangerous mission he's given and resents being treated like a butler by Bane.

DROID PROFILE
Techno-Service Droid

Small but clever mechanicals, Techno-Service Droids take pride in their sophisticated programming and abilities. Their feet have repulsorlifts and can fit together to form a single wheel.

VEHICLE PROFILE
Turbo Tank

Model: HAVw A6 Juggernaut

Class: Wheeled ground vehicle

Weapons:
- Laser cannons, rocket launchers

EPISODE HIGHLIGHT

YOU MAY HAVE MADAME JOCASTA'S SHAPE, BUT NOT HER SKILLS.

Ord Enisence

A hulking Skrilling, Ord Enisence is one of many Jedi sent to battle Separatist forces. But he is killed by the ruthless Bane, and his identity is stolen as part of the hunter's plot to invade the Jedi Temple.

ALIEN PROFILE
Skrillings

Skrillings are brawny aliens native to Agriworld-2079 in the Outer Rim. Despite their fierce appearance, they are known chiefly as relentless beggars and bargainers.

PROFILE
Holocron

Holocrons are ancient crystal lattices created by Force users to store vast amounts of information. Most can only be opened by using the Force – a safeguard against the accidental exposure of the sensitive information within them.

Clawdites

Shape-shifters from the Mid Rim world of Zolan, Clawdites can change their appearance at will. Skilled Clawdites are able to assume forms much larger or smaller than their own bodies.

EPISODE HIGHLIGHT

GUARD DUTY? FOR HOW LONG?

LONGER, NOW.

Jocasta Nu

The Jedi Order's Chief Librarian, Jocasta Nu is a stern taskmaster who demands that her Padawan assistants respect the Order's treasure trove of galactic knowledge.

THERE IS MORE KNOWLEDGE HERE THAN ANYWHERE ELSE IN THE GALAXY.

"Overconfidence is the most dangerous form of carelessness."

SYNOPSIS

Bane has captured the Jedi Bolla Ropal and the Kyber memory crystal, which a Jedi can use to unlock the stolen holocron and retrieve a list of the galaxy's Force-sensitive children. Bane kills Ropal after he refuses to open the holocron, but lures Anakin and Ahsoka on to his frigate. After a wild battle, Bane captures Ahsoka and traps her in an airlock. To save her, Anakin agrees to unlock the holocron, and Bane flees with it. The Jedi barely escape before the frigate explodes, apparently killing Bane and destroying the holocron.

I HAVE A SMALL FAVOUR TO ASK OUR JEDI GUEST.

TRIVIA

The Kyber crystal is used to focus the Force in early drafts of *A New Hope*. The idea was scrapped for the movie, but revisited (as the Kaiburr Crystal) in the 1978 novel *Splinter of the Mind's Eye*.

Bolla Ropal

A Rodian Jedi, Bolla Ropal is the keeper of the Kyber crystal. He has defended the Jedi's secrets for many years, and refuses to let Bane have them, even at the cost of his own life.

Denal

A veteran clone trooper, Denal scuffles with Bane on his doomed frigate and limps aboard the last shuttle to escape the ship. But why is he leaking green blood when they arrive on the *Resolute*?

NEWSREEL

Stolen secrets! Villainous mercenary Cad Bane was hired by Darth Sidious to steal a holocron from the vaults of the Jedi Temple. After fleeing the scene of the crime, Bane hunted down and captured Master Bolla Ropal, who has a crystal which holds secrets of the Jedi Order. As a Separatist fleet arrives to help the bounty hunter, Anakin Skywalker races in to cut off their escape and stop Bane from delivering the stolen holocron . . . ▮

VEHICLE PROFILE
Separatist Frigate

Model: *Munificent*-class Star Frigate

Class: Capital Ship

Weapons:
- Turbolasers
- Laser cannons
- Ion cannons
- Projectile launchers

CARGO OF DOOM

Episode

Koho

Captain Rex sends Denal and Koho to find Anakin and Ahsoka, as Bane's ship begins to disintegrate. But the clone trooper doesn't survive his encounter with the bounty hunter.

EPISODE HIGHLIGHT

> YOU'RE NOT MUCH OF A CHALLENGE, YOUNGLING. I'VE GOT YOU RIGHT WHERE I WANT YOU.

ALIEN PROFILE
Duros

The blue-skinned Duros are a common sight in the galaxy, and have been explorers and hyperspace scouts for thousands of years. The Neimoidians are an ancient offshoot of the Duros species.

WEAPON PROFILE
Stun Cuffs

Bane immobilizes Ahsoka with binders specially designed for Jedi – the more the person wearing them struggles, the tighter they get.

WEAPON PROFILE
Projectile Warhead

Deck cannons fire these powerful warheads, which can punch through enemy ships' armour and destroy incoming fighters. They can explode if jostled or overheated.

BANE'S DEAD... BUT I CAN STILL FEEL HIM.

CHILDREN OF THE FORCE

"The first step to correcting a mistake is patience."

> AMONG THE CHILDREN OF THE JEDI, THERE ARE NO INNOCENTS.

SYNOPSIS

Disguised in clone armour, Bane steals a starfighter and escapes from the Jedi cruiser. Darth Sidious hires him to kidnap Force-sensitive infants, whom Sidious's droids will train as dark side spies. The Jedi capture Bane on Naboo, but not before he seizes two children. Mace and Obi-Wan bring Bane to Black Stall Station, where they retrieve the holocron but lose Bane. Meanwhile, Anakin and Ahsoka retrace Bane's steps to Mustafar, where they rescue the children.

TRIVIA

● The mobile over Roo-Roo Page's crib includes a colo claw fish and a sando aqua monster, two of the beasties that pursued Qui-Gon Jinn, Obi-Wan Kenobi and Jar Jar Binks in *The Phantom Menace*.

Wee Dunn

A Force-sensitive Rodian baby, Wee Dunn is kidnapped by Bane and taken to Mustafar, where nanny droids prepare him to be a subject for Darth Sidious's evil experiments.

NEWSREEL

A thief hunted! In a daring assault, Anakin Skywalker and his Padawan Ahsoka boarded the warship of cunning bounty hunter Cad Bane to recover a stolen holocron containing a list of the galaxy's Force-sensitive children and future Jedi Knights. After a desperate chase and duel with the villain, Anakin and his troops defeated Bane, but were forced to evacuate his doomed vessel without the holocron . . . ∎

Mahtee Dunn

As the mother of a Force-sensitive child, Mahtee Dunn knows she will have to give up her baby for Jedi training. But she is still heartbroken when a hooded figure arrives on Rodia and tells her the time has come.

VEHICLE PROFILE
Xanadu Blood

Model: Modified *Rogue*-class Porax-38 starfighter

Class: Starfighter

Weapons:
- Laser cannons

EPISODE HIGHLIGHT

YOU'RE NO CLONE!

Zinn Toa

Bane kidnapped this young Nautolan from Glee Anselm and transported him to Mustafar, leaving him in the care of RO-Z67. Luckily, Anakin and Ahsoka rescued him before Sidious's plan could be carried out.

PROFILE
Black Stall Station

Black Stall Station is a derelict station in the Rogue Antar system. Cad Bane used it as a hideout, stashing the stolen Jedi holocron there.

PLANET PROFILE
Mustafar

Mustafar is a volcanic world deep in the Outer Rim. Darth Sidious's agents have taken over one of its abandoned mining stations for use as a secret base.

Roo-Roo Page

A Gungan toddler, Roo-Roo Page was one of the Force-sensitive children selected by Darth Sidious for his experiments. But the Jedi beat Bane to Roo-Roo's home on Naboo and foiled her kidnapping.

RO-Z67

RO-Z67 was programmed to be kind to the babies in her care, but Sidious's agents have reprogrammed her to supervise wicked experiments instead. She is helpless to resist such orders.

DROID PROFILE
Nanny Droid

Nanny droids are programmed for childcare and first aid, allowing them to help the galaxy's busy parents. But they can be reprogrammed to do things no parent would ever allow.

EPISODE HIGHLIGHT

LOOK INTO THIS, IT WILL RELAX YOU.

DON'T MOVE, SLEEMO!

YOU WEREN'T THE CHILD I WAS EXPECTING TO FIND.

VEHICLE PROFILE
T-6 Shuttle

Model: Slayn & Korpil T-6 shuttle

Class: Shuttle

Weapons: None

"A true heart should never be doubted."

I SEE NOW WHY YOU RENEWED OUR FRIENDSHIP, SO YOU COULD SPY ON ME AND STEAL FROM ME!

SYNOPSIS

Padmé once had a brief romance with the Banking Clan's Rush Clovis. Now the Jedi suspect Clovis of Separatist ties and recruit Padmé to spy on him. With a disguised Anakin serving as pilot, Padmé accompanies Clovis to Cato Neimoidia, where she discovers he's plotting to build a Separatist droid foundry. She steals a data disc, but is poisoned by Lott Dod. Discovering the theft, Clovis takes the antidote from Dod at gunpoint, intending to trade it for the disc. But Anakin grabs the antidote and flies away with Padmé, leaving Clovis behind to face those he has betrayed.

LANGUAGE LESSON

What did Anakin and Padmé have for dinner? In Aurebesh, the side of the carton says WARM while the top says...

Rush Clovis

A high-ranking member of the Banking Clan and Scipio's Senator, Rush Clovis hopes to rekindle an old romance with Padmé while striking a deal with the Neimoidians to bankroll a new Separatist factory.

Treachery in the Senate! The Jedi Council suspects that Senator Rush Clovis is secretly taking part in a Separatist conspiracy. But to find out what the Senator from Scipio is up to, the Council will need a spy of its own. Meanwhile, Jedi Anakin Skywalker has been away from Coruscant on a lengthy tour of duty leading the clone army. Now Anakin returns for a long-awaited reunion with his wife, Padmé Amidala . . . ∎

Lott Dod

The Trade Federation's representative to the Senate, Lott Dod serves Count Dooku while pretending to help the Senate's peace faction with its efforts to negotiate an end to the war with the Separatists.

VEHICLE PROFILE
Padmé's Star Skiff

Model: Modified Nubia Star Drives J-Type star skiff

Class: Star yacht

Weapons:
• Laser cannons

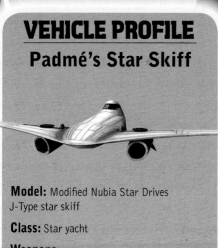

I HAD TO HITCH A RIDE ON A CARGO FREIGHTER.

WHAT HAPPENED TO YOUR MILITARY TRANSPORT?

UH, IT BLEW UP.

PLANET PROFILE
Coruscant

The capital of the Republic, Coruscant's entire surface is covered with skyscrapers, making the whole planet an enormous city populated by trillions of beings.

PROFILE
Hologram Disc

Hologram discs store data in hologram form that can be transferred to or from computer databanks. A single disc can hold vast amounts of information, yet fit in a pocket.

DON'T TAKE IT PERSONALLY, ANAKIN. DUTY COMES FIRST, ESPECIALLY IN WARTIME.

PROFILE
Manax-Root Poison

Manax-root poison is odourless, tasteless and slow-acting, causing a long slide into unconsciousness and then death. This makes it perfect for assassinations and other dark Neimoidian dealings.

LOTT DOD POISONED HER. SHE'S DYING.

PLANET PROFILE
Cato Neimoidia

A lush Neimoidian world in the Colonies, Cato Neimoidia is home only to the richest Neimoidian nobles and their many servants.

I WISH I COULD GIVE YOU THE DISC, BUT I HAVE A LOT OF FAITH IN YOUR SURVIVAL SKILLS.

"Believe in yourself or no one else will."

TO ENSURE THAT GEONOSIS RISE AGAIN DOES NOT, CAPTURE POGGLE WE MUST.

SYNOPSIS

Anakin, Obi-Wan and Ki-Adi-Mundi lead Republic forces in an all-out assault on Geonosis, which is once again supporting the Separatists. In the fierce fighting, both Anakin and Obi-Wan have gunships shot out from under them. Anakin and Ahsoka push on towards the shield protecting Poggle the Lesser's droid foundries, while Obi-Wan must be rescued. After pitched battles, the three-pronged attack succeeds at bringing down the shields, and the way forward is finally clear.

LANGUAGE LESSON

Ki-Adi-Mundi

A Cerean member of the Jedi Council, Ki-Adi-Mundi has a healthy respect for the Geonosians and their forces.

The nexu on the side of Obi-Wan Kenobi's gunship is a BAD KITTY.

Commander Jet

Formally known as CC-1993, Jet serves under Ki-Adi-Mundi, and leads his flame troopers into battle against the winged warriors of the Geonosian hives.

NEWSREEL

Counter-attack! With the clone army stretched in desperate attempt to engage General Grievous' starfleet, Separatist planets that were once thought secure are now rising up against the Republic. On Geonosis, Separatist leader Poggle the Lesser, safe in his newly ray-shielded factories, creates thousands of terrible new weapons which march off the assembly line against the outnumbered clone army. The Jedi, resolute in the effort to restore order to the Republic, mount a massive invasion to retake Geonosis and shut down Poggle's factories once and for all . . . ∎

WEAPON PROFILE
BT X-42 Flamethrower

These heavy weapons are wielded by flame troopers, who are trained to lay down overlapping fans of fire to drive living opponents out of their defensive positions.

Clone Flame Trooper

Flame troopers are trained to resist the natural urge to move away from fire, confident that their insulated gear will keep them safe from harm.

VEHICLE PROFILE
Y-Wing

Model: BTL-B Y-wing starfighter

Class: Starfighter

Weapons:
- Laser cannons
- Ion cannons
- Proton torpedo launchers

THERE IS NO SUCH THING AS LUCK.

Geonosian Warrior

The Geonosian warrior caste is made up of winged fighters, who will lay down their lives if ordered to do so by higher-ranking members of their hive.

WEAPON PROFILE
Sonic Blaster

Sound alone doesn't seem like it would give clone troopers nightmares, but a direct hit from a Geonosian sonic blaster can tear a man apart.

VEHICLE PROFILE
Armoured Assault Tank

Model: Baktoid Armoured Assault Tank

Class: Repulsorcraft

Weapons:
- Laser cannons
- Projectile launchers

VEHICLE PROFILE
Geonosian Fighter

Model: Geonosian *Nantex*-class starfighter

Class: Starfighter

Weapons:
- Laser cannon

"No gift is more precious than trust."

SYNOPSIS

Luminara Unduli decides on a two-part plan to take Poggle's droid foundry: she and Anakin will keep the Geonosians occupied with a frontal assault, while Ahsoka and Barriss Offee infiltrate the foundry through the catacombs and rig it with bombs. After their bombs are disarmed, Barriss and Ahsoka turn the guns of a super tank on the reactor, accepting that the explosion will probably kill them. The blast destroys the foundry and buries the super tank, but after a frantic search, the Padawans are found alive and freed.

> WHEN THE TIME COMES, I AM PREPARED TO LET MY STUDENT GO. CAN YOU SAY THE SAME?

TRIVIA

The nose art on Luminara Unduli's gunship is to the point: A clone trooper's boot connects with the backside of Separatist leader Count Dooku.

Barriss Offee

Trained by the no-nonsense Jedi Luminara Unduli, Barriss Offee is an obedient, dutiful Padawan. She forms an unlikely friendship with the brash Ahsoka Tano.

NEWSREEL

The final surge! Having learned of warlord Poggle the Lesser's plot to rebuild a Separatist droid foundry on Geonosis, Jedi Knight Anakin Skywalker and his Padawan, Ahsoka Tano, prepare to assault this heavily-fortified installation. Their mission: destroy the factory at all cost. Anticipating stiff resistance, Republic commanders send Jedi Master Luminara Unduli and her Padawan, Barriss Offee, to reinforce the attack. But time runs short for our intrepid heroes as the dreaded droid mill nears completion . . . ∎

Poggle the Lesser

The Archduke of Geonosis and a high-ranking member of the Techno Union, Poggle is one of the leaders of the Separatist movement.

EPISODE HIGHLIGHT

PADAWAN LEARNER BARRISS OFFEE, AT YOUR SERVICE.

GLAD TO MEET YOU. I'M AHSOKA.

VEHICLE PROFILE
Super Tank

Model: Baktoid Prototype super tank

Class: Repulsorcraft

Weapons:
- Rapid-fire laser cannons
- Warhead launchers

WEAPONS FACTORY

TX-21

A tactical droid who assists Poggle the Lesser, TX-21 takes a rather unmechanical delight in unleashing the Separatists' new Super Tanks against the Republic.

PROFILE
Comlink

These portable devices are essential for maintaining communications in a busy galaxy. Comlinks come in many forms, from simple hand-held models for civilians to encrypted communicators built into clone armour.

ALIEN PROFILE
Mirialans

These near-humans are native to Mirial, a dry world in the Outer Rim. The Force runs strong in Mirialans, and many Mirialan Jedi preserve their world's styles and traditions, such as facial tattoos.

WHATEVER YOU'RE DOING, I HOPE IT WORKS - BECAUSE I'D SURE RATHER HAVE DIED FIGHTING UP THERE THAN STARVE TO DEATH DOWN HERE.

DON'T WORRY. WE'LL RUN OUT OF AIR LONG BEFORE WE STARVE.

THAT'S A COMFORTING THOUGHT, THANKS.

LOOKS LIKE THE SEPARATISTS HAVE A NEW TOY.

COLLECT THEIR PATHETIC LITTLE BOMBS. THEN WE WILL KILL THEM.

PROFILE
Chronometer

Chronometers keep time, and are found in a huge number of devices used throughout the galaxy. They are particularly important for coordinating simultaneous action by different military units.

ALIEN PROFILE
Geonosians

This insect species dwells in hives on Geonosis, a rocky world near Tatooine. Geonosians are skilled designers whose products include the B1 battle droid. Their castes include flightless worker drones, winged warriors and rarely glimpsed queens.

"Sometimes, accepting help is harder than offering it."

SYNOPSIS

Luminara tracks Poggle the Lesser to the damaged Progate Temple. After losing contact with her, Obi-Wan and Anakin lead a rescue mission. They battle undead Geonosian warriors in the Temple's catacombs, and find Luminara held captive by Karina the Great, the secret Geonosian queen. The dead Geonosians are animated by parasitic brain worms, which Karina plans to use to possess the Jedi. But Anakin and Obi-Wan free Luminara and fight their way back to the surface, leaving Karina buried in the rubble.

WHAT WERE THOSE THINGS? WE COULDN'T KILL THEM!

Karina the Great

The hidden queen of the Geonosians, Karina dwells in the catacombs beneath the Progate Temple, defended by undead Geonosians.

NEWSREEL

Victory on Geonosis! After a massive planetary siege, the Separatist forces on Geonosis have finally fallen. Key weapons factories have been destroyed, but at a heavy cost to Republic troops. Now, as Jedi Master Luminara Unduli and Obi-Wan Kenobi begin a clean-up of the planet, they launch an intense campaign to find Separatist leader Poggle the Lesser and bring him to justice . . . ▪

EPISODE HIGHLIGHT

THAT IS ONE UGLY BUG.

WEAPON PROFILE
Sonic Cannon

A bigger version of the feared Geonosian sonic blaster, the LR1K cannon is effective against larger groupings of attackers, concussing and killing them with sound.

Buzz

A clone trooper, Buzz accompanies Luminara Unduli to the Progate Temple, where he meets an untimely end.

ALIEN PROFILE
Cereans

These cone-headed aliens have a second heart that pumps blood to their oversized brains. Their homeworld, Cerea, is located in the Mid Rim near the galactic frontier.

Undead Geonosians

Brain worms allow a powerful hive mind to control the bodies of Geonosian warriors, even after their deaths.

Gearshift

At the Progate Temple, Gearshift is sent back to the surface to fetch Republic reinforcements. But terrible things are waiting for him in the shadowy catacombs.

AND YOU THINK THAT'S WHY WE COULDN'T KILL THEM? BECAUSE THEY'RE –

– ALREADY DEAD, YES.

PROFILE
Containment Field

Containment fields confine prisoners within a magnetic field, rendering them helpless. They are particularly useful to Separatists because they interfere with a Jedi's connection to the Force.

ALIEN PROFILE
Brain Worms

These worms emerge from eggs laid by a Geonosian queen, and defend her hive by animating the husks of dead Geonosians or seizing control of invaders' brains.

"Attachment is not compassion."

> LET'S JUST SAY MY MASTER WILL ALWAYS DO WHAT NEEDS TO BE DONE.

SYNOPSIS

Ahsoka and Barriss accompany Tango Company aboard a Republic medical frigate to Ord Cestus, not knowing that brain worms are infecting the clone troopers. The Padawans must fight off possessed clones as new worms spread the infection, eventually taking over Barriss's mind as well. After a brief battle with Barriss, Ahsoka contacts Anakin, who has interrogated Poggle and learned cold incapacitates the worms. Ahsoka ruptures the coolant systems, overcoming Barriss and the clones.

Scythe

The first clone from Tango Company to be infected by a brain worm, Scythe carries a backpack full of eggs aboard medical frigate TB-73, intending to spread the contagion to his comrades.

TRIVIA

In the Republic military, it's easy to remember whom you work for: the spoked Republic logo adorns both the Padawans' pillows and the clones' undersuits.

VEHICLE PROFILE
Cargo Frigate TB-73

Model: Kuat Drive Yards *Pelta*-class frigate

Class: Frigate

Weapons:
- Turbolasers
- Laser cannons

NEWSREEL

Victory on Geonosis! After a massive assault, the Republic has finally recaptured the Separatist planet and shut down its droid factories of doom. An investigation by Luminara Unduli led to the discovery of Queen Karina the Great, whose hive mind could reanimate dead Geonosian soldiers. During the destruction of the Queen's temple, the Jedi apprehended her advisor Poggle the Lesser, and now prepare to deliver the villain to Coruscant for trial . . . ∎

EPISODE HIGHLIGHT

Ox

An infected Ox accompanies Edge to ambush Ahsoka and Barriss – the Padawans' first hint that something has gone terribly wrong aboard their ship.

I'M AFRAID WE HAVE A COMPLICATION.

DON'T WE ALWAYS?

Havoc

After he's infected by a brain worm, Havoc joins Scythe, Ox, Edge and Trap to expose the rest of Tango Company's clone troopers to the brain invaders.

THERE YOU ARE, YOU CAN'T HIDE FROM ME.

Trap

Tango Company's commanding officer, Trap responds to the sound of shots and is nearly cut down by a nervous Ahsoka and Barriss, who have just been attacked by Ox and Edge. But Trap isn't infected. At least, not yet ...

PROFILE
Tractor Beam

Tractor beams project force fields that drag objects towards the beam generator. They are used by warships to capture enemy starships, and by tugs guiding ships in for safe dockings.

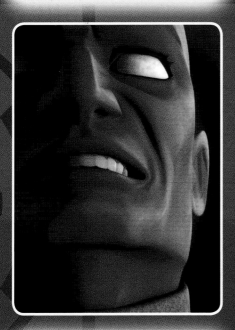

I DON'T NEED MIND TRICKS TO GET YOU TO TALK.

VEHICLE PROFILE
Space Tug

Model: MandalMotors interstellar tug

Class: Space transport

Weapons:
- None

PROFILE
Ord Cestus Medical Station

This Republic space station is one of many that tends to wounded clones and serves as a storehouse for badly needed medical supplies.

"For everything you gain, you lose something else."

SYNOPSIS

THE STORY OF
OBI-WAN KENOBI
ENDS HERE!

General Grievous captures Eeth Koth and
tortures him during a live recording beamed
to the Jedi Temple. Koth signals to the Jedi
that he's in the Saleucami system, and they
rush to rescue him. Obi-Wan allows his ship
to be captured by Grievous and fights the
cyborg warlord, while Anakin and Adi Gallia
try to find Koth. Grievous's plan to trap
the Jedi fails, but he escapes and flees to
Saleucami, with Obi-Wan in hot pursuit.

TRIVIA

Adi Gallia

A wise diplomat and tough fighter, Adi Gallia
is amused and a bit impressed by Anakin's
brash ways, paying little attention to the
disapproval of other high-ranking Jedi.

- The shot of Admiral Yularen on
  the *Resolute's* bridge, ordering the
  fleet to attack, mimics a shot in
  The Empire Strikes Back, in which
  Captain Needa issues orders on the
  bridge of the Star Destroyer Avenger.

Eeth Koth

A member of the Jedi Council, Eeth Koth expects no mercy when he falls into the hands of the pitiless steel warlord General Grievous.

EETH KOTH, ISN'T IT? I'VE BEEN LOOKING FORWARD TO MEETING YOU. HA HA HA!

YOUR REPUTATION PRECEDES YOU, GENERAL. THE REPUTATION OF A COWARD, AND A MURDERER.

MURDERER? IS IT MURDER TO RID THE GALAXY OF YOU JEDI FILTH?

NEWSREEL

Diabolical defeat! Though Republic victories outnumber their losses, the Jedi have been unable to stop Separatist advances in the Outer Rim. The ever-elusive General Grievous stays one step ahead of his opponents. With thousands of droid armies at his command, the Jedi can never predict where Grievous will strike next . . . until now . . . ■

WEAPON PROFILE
Electrostaff

Electrostaffs are made of durable phrik alloy and tipped with electromagnetic pulse generators. MagnaGuards can spin their staffs into deadly circles of energy.

ALIEN PROFILE
Zabraks

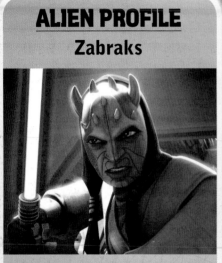

Zabraks are native to the Mid Rim world of Iridonia, and known for the crown of vestigial horns that adorn their heads.

VEHICLE PROFILE
Separatist Destroyer

Model: Hoersch-Kessel/Free Dac *Recusant*-class light destroyer

Class: Capital ship

Weapons:
- Turbolasers
- Laser cannons
- Point-defence laser cannons
- Fighter complement

I HEAR A LOT OF TALKING, GENERAL. BUT IN THE FINAL ACCOUNTING, WHAT DOES ALL THE TALK GET YOU? A FUTILE QUEST FOR POWER? A MUTILATED BODY? AND YOUR PLACE AS DOOKU'S ERRAND BOY!

Captain Lock

Lock serves Eeth Koth aboard his Jedi cruiser, and protests against his commander's orders that he and his men flee to the doomed warship's escape pods.

Model: Kuat Drive Yards *Arquitens*-class light cruiser

Class: Escort cruiser

Weapons:
- Laser cannons

Model: Cygnus Spaceworks *Eta*-class shuttle

Class: Shuttle

Weapons:
- Laser cannons

TV-94

A tactical droid serving Grievous, TV-94 was put in charge of the General's plan to trap the Jedi sent to rescue Eeth Koth. The plan might have worked if someone had been able to lend TV-94 a hand.

EPISODE HIGHLIGHT

SYNOPSIS

Obi-Wan and a squad of clone troopers
land on Saleucami and split up in pursuit
of Grievous, who is searching for an
escape pod with an intact transmitter.
After commando droids ambush Rex and
shoot him in the chest, his troopers leave
him to recover on a farm run by Suu
Lawquane and her husband, Cut —
a deserter from the clone army. When
commando droids attack the farm, Rex
and Cut must team up to destroy them.
Meanwhile, Grievous slips away once again.

> SO, I SEE THE WAR
> HAS FINALLY MADE ITS
> WAY OUT HERE.

LANGUAGE LESSON

The tattoos on Kix's shaved head
spell out A GOOD DROID IS A
DEAD ONE.

Cut Lawquane

A clone who deserted the Republic army,
Cut has sought a better life as a farmer on
Saleucami with Suu and her children, and
hopes the war remains far from his door.

NEWSREEL

Fugitive! Though the Republic has won many decisive battles against the Separatist army in the Outer Rim, the Jedi have failed to capture the elusive General Grievous. After specifically targeting members of the Jedi Council, a trap was set. But following a fierce confrontation, the droid general managed to escape to the surface of the planet Saleucami. Now, the chase is on as General Kenobi leads a squadron of clone troopers and closes in on his desperate target . . . ▌

Suu Lawquane

A Twi'lek farmer, Suu is glad to have found a stepfather for her two children, but fears that one day Cut's past will catch up with him.

EPISODE HIGHLIGHT

HOW COULD YOUR POWER CELLS BE SO DEPLETED?

YOU WOULD NOT LET US RIDE ON ONE OF THOSE CREATURES WITH YOU, SIR. IF YOU WOULD ALLOW US TO CLOSE DOWN FOR A FEW MO –

ANY MORE COMPLAINTS?

UH, NO. NOPE. NO. I DON'T THINK SO. NO.

VEHICLE PROFILE
C-9979 Landing Craft

Model: Haor Chall Engineering C-9979 landing craft

Class: Landing craft

Weapons:
- Laser cannons

ALIEN PROFILE
Reeks

Thick-skinned, horned beasts, reeks have an undeserved reputation for viciousness! They're herbivores, can be trained, and are generally placid if treated with kindness.

ALIEN PROFILE
Eopies

These smelly, dim-witted beasts of burden can live in many climates and eat almost anything, making them useful livestock on farm worlds from Tatooine to Saleucami.

PLANET PROFILE
Saleucami

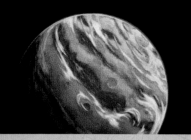

A trading post in the Outer Rim, Saleucami is covered with scars from ancient asteroid impacts. Some of those craters are immense, and shelter oases carpeted with grasses and trees.

EPISODE HIGHLIGHT

WE WANT NO TROUBLE HERE.

EASY WITH THAT WEAPON, MA'AM. WE'RE HERE AS FRIENDS.

> I KNOW YOU THINK I'M A COWARD, REX, BUT BELIEVE ME, I'LL FIGHT TO MY LAST BREATH TO KEEP THEM SAFE.

Kix

A medic serving with Rex's squad on Saleucami, Kix tends to his captain's wounds and orders him to rest on the Lawquane farm while he heals.

Jekk and Shaeeh Lawquane

Suu's young children are delighted when newcomers interrupt the boring routine of farm life. But not all visitors are friendly — there are evil things prowling in their fields.

PROFILE
Dejarik

This ancient game is played on a hologame table, with three-dimensional playing pieces that resemble real and imaginary creatures. Dejarik is beloved across the galaxy by nobles and simple folk alike.

LIGHTSABER LOST

> "Easy isn't always simple."

> THIS WEAPON IS YOUR LIFE.

SYNOPSIS

After a pickpocket steals her lightsaber, Ahsoka seeks the help of the elderly Jedi Tera Sinube, an expert in the Coruscant underworld. Tracking the lost lightsaber, Ahsoka and Tera stumble on the scene of a murder and find a terrified girl in hiding – and Ahsoka's lightsaber in the hands of the criminal Cassie Cryar. Ahsoka chases Cassie across the cityscape, but Cassie takes hostages aboard a hover train. Tera appears and ends the standoff, disarming Cassie and returning Ahsoka's saber.

TRIVIA

- One of the mugshots studied by Ahsoka and Jocasta is that of Brea Tonnika, glimpsed alongside her "twin" Senni in the Mos Eisley cantina in *A New Hope*.

Bannamu

A Patrolian pickpocket, Bannamu steals Ahsoka's lightsaber and sells it after nearly slicing off a fin with the unfamiliar weapon.

NEWSREEL

War creates opportunities for the criminal underworld! Ruthless mercenaries conspire with the Separatists to disrupt and exploit the unstable situation within the Republic.

Now, Anakin Skywalker and Ahsoka Tano descend into the treacherous gangster havens, in an effort to find a corrupt and vile arms dealer who is buying weapons on the black market and selling them to the Republic's enemies . . . ∎

Tera Sinube

An elderly Cosian Jedi, Tera Sinube is an expert on Coruscant's criminals. A lifetime of experience has taught him that wisdom is better than haste.

TIME TO DIE!

VEHICLE PROFILE
Hover Train

Model: Kuat Drive Yards 6-B hover train

Class: Repulsorcraft

Weapons:
• None

FOR A GUY THAT MOVES SLOW, YOU ALWAYS SEEM TO GET AHEAD OF ME.

THE VALUE OF MOVING SLOWLY IS THAT ONE CAN ALWAYS CLEARLY SEE THE WAY AHEAD.

ALIEN PROFILE
Patrolians

A diminutive aquatic species, Patrolians move swiftly and silently, making them well-suited to careers as spies, pickpockets and saboteurs.

WEAPON PROFILE
Sabercane

Stooped old Tera Sinube doesn't look threatening as he leans on his cane in the streets of Coruscant. But the tip of his cane is also the hilt of his lightsaber – which he wields with surprising speed.

Ione Marcy

Ione Marcy appears to be an innocent girl shocked by the murder of her friend Nack Movers. But she's secretly in league with the vicious Cassie Cryar.

Cassie Cryar

An agile Terrellian Jango Jumper, Cassie leads Ahsoka on a dizzying chase across the rooftops of Coruscant, the Padawan's stolen lightsaber blazing in one hand.

ALIEN PROFILE
Ithorians

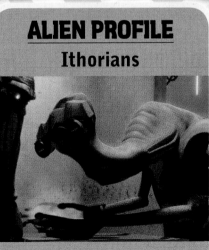

Nicknamed "Hammerheads," most Ithorians are peaceful creatures who love nature. But some have made less wholesome lives for themselves in Coruscant's seedier districts.

SO YOU WANT TO BUY A LIGHTSABER? HOW MUCH ARE YOU WILLING TO PAY?

THE MANDALORE PLOT

Episode 12

"If you ignore the past, you jeopardize your future."

SYNOPSIS

Obi-Wan visits Mandalore to investigate rumours that the planet has returned to its war-like past. Duchess Satine tells him of a cult called Death Watch, dismissing them as hooligans, but Obi-Wan and Satine witness a Death Watch bombing carried out by a native of the moon Concordia. On the moon, Obi-Wan slips away from Governor Pre Vizsla and is ambushed by Death Watch warriors. Satine rescues him, but the two are confronted by Vizsla, revealed as Death Watch's leader. Obi-Wan defeats Vizsla in a duel and he and Satine escape.

MY ANCESTORS FOUGHT PROUDLY AS WARRIORS AGAINST THE JEDI. NOW, THAT WOMAN TARNISHES THE VERY NAME MANDALORIAN.

Mandalorian Guard

Satine is kept safe by her Mandalorian Guard, whose helmets evoke the planet's warrior tradition, even as their training stresses defence and restraint.

Duchess Satine

The leader of Mandalore and the Council of Neutral Systems, Duchess Satine is a passionate voice for peace in the galaxy – a brave stand that has made her many enemies.

Model: MandalMotors *Kom'rk*-class fighter/transport

Class: Space transport

Weapons:
- Laser cannons
- Torpedo launcher

EPISODE HIGHLIGHT

NEWSREEL

Diplomacy or deception? The Council of Neutral Systems speaks for over 1,500 worlds who want to stay out of the war. But rumours have reached the Republic Senate suggesting that the Council's new leader – Duchess Satine of Mandalore – is secretly building her own army to fight for the Separatist cause!

Now, Jedi Master Obi-Wan Kenobi has been sent to Mandalore to discover the truth behind these claims . . . ▪

PLANET PROFILE
Concordia

A moon of Mandalore, Concordia was once despoiled by extensive mining operations, but generations of peace have filled most of the scars with greenery.

Prime Minister Almec

A tall, dignified diplomat, Almec takes pride in Mandalore's efforts to put its violent past behind it and create a peaceful, technological culture.

TRIVIA

Pre Vizsla's name is a play on "pre-vis," an animation tool that uses a virtual camera to manipulate characters, ships and settings on a computer.

PROFILE
Death Watch

Not all Mandalorians support Satine. An underground group called Death Watch wears traditional Mandalorian armour and seeks to restore the values once held by the planet's nomadic warrior clans.

Pre Vizsla

The governor of Concordia, Vizsla is secretly the leader of Death Watch, and seeks to overthrow Satine and ally Mandalore with the Separatists.

PLANET PROFILE
Mandalore

An Outer Rim world, Mandalore was devastated by a war with the Jedi centuries ago. Many of its people now dwell in cube-like cities that showcase the peaceful use of Mandalorian technology.

"Fear not for the future, weep not for the past."

SYNOPSIS

En route to Coruscant, Satine meets with four Senators aboard the *Coronet*. Assassin droids escape from a container in the hold, killing two clone troopers and hunting the passengers. Anakin discovers the container had a Senate seal and realizes one of the Senators is a traitor. Obi-Wan uses a captive assassin droid to determine that the traitor is Tal Merrik. He holds Satine at gunpoint and brandishes a remote – he's wired the *Coronet*'s engines to blow. As battle droids board the *Coronet*, Satine frees herself and turns the tables on Merrik. He scoffs that neither Satine nor Obi-Wan can kill him in cold blood – and is struck down from behind by Anakin.

WAR IS INTOLERABLE.

DROID PROFILE
Service Droids

Not every protocol droid gets to spend their days hobnobbing with diplomats. Some are stuck performing routine tasks on starships and in spaceports, such as supervising the loading of cargo and checking it against manifests.

NEWSREEL

A royal welcome! Sent to investigate allegations that Mandalore was joining Count Dooku's Separatists, Obi-Wan Kenobi was reunited with an old friend, the Duchess Satine of Kalevala. While Satine claimed Mandalore's intentions were to remain neutral during the war, an attack on the capital city led Obi-Wan to the discovery of a terrorist organization known as Death Watch. Now the Duchess travels to the Senate, so she can plead her case against her involvement in the war, as the Jedi prepare a defence against her opponents . . . ∎

EPISODE HIGHLIGHT

SENATORS, I PRESUME YOU ARE ACQUAINTED WITH THE COLLECTION OF HALF-TRUTHS AND HYPERBOLE KNOWN AS OBI-WAN KENOBI?

YOUR HIGHNESS IS TOO KIND.

Tal Merrik

Merrik is Kalevala's Senator and an old friend of Duchess Satine. But his secret allegiance is to Death Watch.

Redeye

Redeye is assigned to the boring duty of inspecting cargo containers aboard the *Coronet*. But one of those containers holds a terrible secret . . .

I'LL TAKE CARE OF THIS, OBI-WAN. YOU GO FIND YOUR GIRLFRIEND.

RIGHT. UH ... NO, ANAKIN, SHE'S NOT MY ...

I'VE LOVED YOU FROM THE MOMENT YOU CAME TO MY AID ALL THOSE YEARS AGO.

VEHICLE PROFILE
The *Coronet*

Model: Kalevala Spaceworks custom luxury liner

Class: Space transport

Weapons:
- Laser cannons
- Ion cannons

DROID PROFILE
Assassin Droids

Death Watch sneaks spider-like assassin probe droids aboard the *Coronet*. That's a nasty surprise, but there's worse: as a backup, the droids are filled with miniature assassins.

Mixer

Mixer tries to liven up inspection duty by warning Redeye to be careful in the dark. But that joke soon doesn't seem so funny ...

WEAPON PROFILE
Deactivator

Used primarily as a means of self-defence, deactivator pistols can disrupt droid circuitry and fry the electronics of blasters and other weapons.

Kin Robb

A Senator from the city-planet Taris, Kin Robb fears her world will be attacked by the Separatists and has aligned herself with Satine's peace movement.

"In war, truth is the first casualty."

SYNOPSIS

On Coruscant, Palpatine plays a hologram of a Mandalorian minister seemingly pleading for Republic intervention. Despite Satine's protests that something isn't right, the Republic prepares to send military forces to her world. Satine secretly meets with a Republic intelligence operative, who tells her the hologram has been altered and slips her a disc of the true recording – just before he's gunned down by an assassin. Satine eludes the assassin and turns herself in, buying time for Obi-Wan to take the disc to Padmé. She plays it for the Senate, revealing the plot and averting war.

SOMETIMES THE LINE BETWEEN FRIEND AND FOE IS BLURRED.

Deputy Minister Jerec

A friend of Satine's, Jerec is killed by Death Watch shortly after sending a message pleading for Republic intervention on Mandalore. But is that really what he said?

TRIVIA

The shields carried by Coruscant's Riot Clone Troopers are similar to those carried by stormtroopers in Ralph McQuarrie's concept paintings for *A New Hope*.

NEWSREEL

A diplomatic mission! As dissent threatens to tear apart the peaceful Mandalore system, Duchess Satine struggles to protect her people against the escalating violence. Betrayed by two of her trusted allies, Satine now travels to Coruscant. There, she hopes to convince the Senate that a destructive splinter group, Death Watch, does not represent the entire Mandalorian government . . . ▮

PROFILE
Mandalorian Scouts

Servants of Satine's government, Mandalorian scouts pursue a dangerous mission: find Death Watch's armies and report back on their doings.

EPISODE HIGHLIGHT

SOMEONE TRIED TO KILL ME. THE CONTROLS ON MY SPEEDER WERE COMPROMISED.

SADLY, MY DEAR, THERE IS NO PROOF ANYONE TAMPERED WITH ANYTHING. I AM AFRAID IT MIGHT HAVE BEEN JUST AN ACCIDENT.

AN ACCIDENT? AND IT JUST HAPPENED TO COINCIDE WITH ME DEFENDING MY HOMEWORLD.

Aramis

A long-time member of Satine's Guard, Aramis pilots the Duchess's speeder through the cityscape of Coruscant.

DROID PROFILE
Security Droid

These flying droids respond to emergencies on Coruscant, identifying suspects and guiding police droids and military personnel to their location.

ALIEN PROFILE
Chagrians

These blue-skinned beings hail from Champala in the Inner Rim. Lethorns grow from the top and sides of their heads.

EPISODE HIGHLIGHT

DEATH WATCH IS PREPARED TO FIGHT?

YES, THE PEOPLE HAVE BEEN WORKED INTO SUCH A FRENZY THAT WHEN THE REPUBLIC DOES ARRIVE, THE DEATH WATCH WILL BE CONSIDERED HEROES.

EXCELLENT.

Davu Golec

A bureaucrat working for the Republic's Ministry of Intelligence, Golec discovers someone is faking evidence in an effort to start a war with Mandalore.

PROFILE
Riot Clone Troopers

These troopers are specially trained to control crowds with non-lethal weapons, and provide backup to Coruscant's regular police in case of trouble.

EPISODE HIGHLIGHT

SUPREME CHANCELLOR! THERE HAS BEEN A DEVELOPMENT IN THE CASE FOR MANDALORE'S NEUTRALITY.

THE CHAIR RECOGNIZES THE SENATOR FROM NABOO.

I THINK THIS SHOULD CAST A NEW LIGHT ON THE SO-CALLED EVIDENCE WE SAW EARLIER.

THE SENATE MURDERS

"Searching for the truth is easy. Accepting the truth is hard."

SYNOPSIS

Padmé proposes that the Senate cut military spending, despite strong opposition from Kamino's Halle Burtoni. While she is celebrating the speech with her allies, Onaconda Farr dies of an apparent heart attack. A bumbling detective, Tan Divo, says the Rodian was murdered and begins an investigation. Suspicion falls on Burtoni, but she proclaims her innocence. Divo determines that Farr was killed by a Kaminoan poison that only affects Rodians and plans to arrest Burtoni. But the killer is revealed to be Lolo Purs, Rodia's representative, who was angered by Farr's brief flirtation with the Separatists.

MURDER. IT'S INCONCEIVABLE.

Lolo Purs

A Rodian Representative, Lolo assists her mentor, Senator Onaconda Farr, in his legislative work on Coruscant.

EPISODE HIGHLIGHT

YOU SHOULDN'T MAKE SPEECHES LIKE THAT. IT'S UNPATRIOTIC.

THE ONLY THING I FIND UNPATRIOTIC IS YOUR WARMONGERING.

Mon Mothma

A Senator from the Core World of Chandrila, Mon Mothma works for peace, convinced that no military solution can bring an end to the war.

DROID PROFILE
Police Droid

These mechanicals keep order on Coruscant and other Republic worlds, and are programmed to detect illegal activity and apprehend criminals. They do so peacefully if possible, using their blasters as a last resort.

NEWSREEL

War on many fronts! While battles are fought by clones in the field, a different war is waged in the Galactic Senate. As heavy losses add up, a group of Senators led by Halle Burtoni of Kamino propose an escalation of troop production. Senator Padmé Amidala, recognizing that more troops will only prolong the fighting, works tirelessly with her allies to introduce a bill to cut military spending and stop the creation of more clone troopers . . . ■

Halle Burtoni

Halle Burtoni represents Kamino, the planet that produces the Republic's clone armies, and pushes the Senate to vote for more military spending.

THANK YOU, SENATOR ... AMIDALA, IS IT?

BUT I ALREADY HAVE MY THEORY AND I'LL FOLLOW MY HUNCH IF YOU DON'T MIND.

AFTER ALL, I AM THE INSPECTOR, YOU'RE THE SENATOR, SO I'LL HANDLE THE INSPECTING, AND YOU CAN STICK TO THE . . . SENATING.

EVERY TIME ONO OPENED HIS BEFUDDLED MOUTH, IT GAVE US ANOTHER QUOTE TO USE IN OUR FUNDRAISING. WHY WOULD WE KILL OUR BEST SOURCE OF INCOME?

Tan Divo

A bumbling police inspector, Tan Divo is sent to the Senate to investigate the murder of Onaconda Farr. It's a job Divo fears will generate a lot of paperwork.

Mee Deechi

A Senator from Umbara, Mee Deechi is a close ally of Burtoni, and opposes any attempt to cut funding for the fight against the Separatists.

"A wise leader knows when to follow."

IT'S BEEN SO LONG SINCE I HAD A WORTHY OPPONENT.

SYNOPSIS

At Christophsis, Obi-Wan tells Anakin to stop trying to break the Separatist blockade, as he has a way to change the Republic strategy – a stealth ship hidden by a cloaking device. But Anakin must outwit Admiral Trench, a Separatist commander legendary for his brilliance. After a brief skirmish, Trench taunts Anakin that he's faced cloaked vessels before, prompting Obi-Wan to discover that Trench's strategy for destroying such ships is to home in on them with flights of torpedos. Anakin tricks Trench into firing, then turns and rushes for Trench's ship, which is destroyed by its own missiles.

Admiral Trench

A legendary Separatist commander, Trench was believed killed at the Battle of Malastare Narrows. But he is very much alive – and hungers for a challenge worthy of his reputation.

An impenetrable defence. Separatist ships blockade the resource-rich planet of Christophsis, trapping Senator Bail Organa and his relief effort. Desperate to aid the esteemed Senator, a Republic task force under the command of Jedi Knight Anakin Skywalker must break the impasse. But time runs short for the Senator and the good citizens of Christophsis . . . ■

Blackout

A stealth clone trooper, Blackout has trained extensively on the Republic's new stealth ship, and is eager to see how it performs in combat.

VEHICLE PROFILE
Invincible

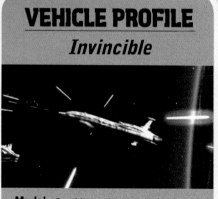

Model: *Providence*-class carrier/destroyer

Class: Capital ship

Weapons:
- Turbolasers
- Ion cannons
- Point-defence lasercannons
- Torpedos

VEHICLE PROFILE
Republic Stealth Ship

Model: Sienar Design Systems experimental stealth ship

Class: Corvette

Weapons:
- Torpedos
- Point-defence cannons

ALIEN PROFILE
Harch

Eight-limbed beings from the Mid Rim world Secundus Ando, the Harch are believed to be an offshoot of the Aqualish, and have often employed armies of Aqualish mercenaries in their bloody civil wars.

PROFILE
Stealth Clone Troopers

These clones have been specially trained as part of the Republic's secret programme to create stealth warships, and take pride in their distinctive black armour.

Bail Organa

The Senator from Alderaan, Bail leads a relief mission to the embattled world of Christophsis, only to find himself trapped by a Separatist blockade.

PROFILE
Cloaking Device

Cloaking devices make starships invisible to both the naked eye and starship sensors. They require massive amounts of energy to function, limiting their effectiveness in battle.

Spark

A rookie member of the stealth squad, Spark awaits his chance to prove himself to his new squadmates.

EPISODE HIGHLIGHT

HMM. SOMETHING ODD IS GOING ON OUT THERE.

DISENGAGE CLOAKING DEVICE.

THERE! A CLOAKED SHIP!

FIRE!

"Courage makes heroes, but trust builds friendship."

SYNOPSIS

Stranded on Felucia, Anakin, Obi-Wan and Ahsoka find a spice-farming village defended by Sugi's band of mercenaries. The Jedi accuse the mercenaries of exploiting the villagers, but Sugi insists that their commitment to defend the villagers against a marauding pirate gang is genuine. When the pirates attack, the Jedi join Sugi's band and the villagers and drive them off.

> I WILL KEEP THESE PEOPLE SAFE – MY WAY.

Sugi

A Zabrak mercenary, Sugi and her gang are paid by Felucia's villagers to safeguard their spice crop – a task Sugi vows to carry out to the best of her ability.

TRIVIA

Sharp-eyed fans will note this episode begins with a separate "title card." This touch, unique in the series, is a tribute to *Seven Samurai* director Akira Kurosawa.

Embo

A Kyuzo warrior from Phatrong, Embo is a deadly shot with a bowcaster, as Gwarm's pirates soon discover.

NEWSREEL

The death toll rises! As the battles intensify and threaten a growing number of Republic worlds, planets are left to survive on their own while the Jedi struggle to fight a war on many fronts. A series of medical stations have been established as a lifeline for those in need. But the facilities are easy prey for Separatist attacks. After losing contact with the medical station orbiting Felucia, Obi-Wan Kenobi, Anakin Skywalker and Ahsoka Tano are sent to investigate . . . ■

EPISODE HIGHLIGHT

YOU ALWAYS TAUGHT ME TO GO ON INSTINCT, AND MY INSTINCTS TELL ME TO GO THAT WAY.

WELL, THAT ... THAT DOESN'T SEEM RIGHT. I THINK WE SHOULD GO THIS WAY.

WHY DO YOU EVEN ASK FOR MY OPINION? YOU NEVER DO THINGS MY WAY.

WE CRASHED THE SHIP YOUR WAY.

VEHICLE PROFILE
Halo

Model: Modified Botajef Shipyards SS-54 light freighter

Class: Space transport

Weapons:
- Laser cannons

Rumi Paramita

A Frenk from Gorobei, Rumi is Sugi's second-in-command. Beneath her cheerful disposition is a keen mind with an excellent grasp of military tactics.

Seripas

A hulking figure in scarred armour, Seripas looks terrifying. But where warriors are concerned, sometimes there is less than meets the eye.

PLANET PROFILE
Felucia

A forested world in the Outer Rim, Felucia is alive with brilliantly coloured trees and fungi. Its farmers grow valuable crops, including the rare spice known as nysillim.

Gwarm

A ruthless lieutenant to the infamous pirate Hondo Ohnaka, Gwarm's philosophy is simple: if he wants something, he takes it.

YOU KNOW WHAT I ALWAYS SAY – SPEAK SOFTLY AND DRIVE A BIG TANK.

VEHICLE PROFILE
Vulture Droid

Model: Self-propelled fattle droid mark I

Class: Droid starfighter

Weapons:
- Blaster cannons
- Missiles

PLANET PROFILE
Bowcaster

These weapons fire explosive quarrels and require great strength to wield. Wookiees and Kyuzo are two species strong enough to do so.

> "Choose what is right, not what is easy."

I HAVE A BAD FEELING ABOUT THIS.

SYNOPSIS

Republic forces battling on Malastare detonate a massive bomb that creates a giant sinkhole, trapping many clone troopers and freeing a giant Zillo Beast. The native Dugs demand Republic help killing the Beast, which Palpatine grants over Mace's objections. But Anakin has another idea: stun the Beast so the Dugs only think it's dead and then transport it offworld. Palpatine agrees and the plan succeeds, but Palpatine orders the Beast brought to Coruscant for further study.

NEWSREEL

Desperate times call for desperate measures! In one of the longest and fiercest battles of the war, Separatist forces are on the verge of claiming the planet Malastare. If the Republic loses this planet, it will cost them vital fuel resources necessary for maintaining their armies. In a final effort to turn the tide of this battle, Supreme Chancellor Palpatine has authorized the use of the Republic's newest weapon: the electro-proton bomb. Now at the imperial palace of Doge Urus, the leader of the Dugs, the Jedi count down the minutes until the detonation of their doomsday device . . . ▮

The Zillo Beast

These great beasts once roamed the surface of Malastare, and were thought to be extinct – but at least one survived. Studying the Beast's indestructible scales could help the Republic military produce stronger, lighter armour.

VEHICLE PROFILE
Stun Tank

Model: Rothana Heavy Engineering RX-200 *Falchion*-Class assault tank

Class: Repulsorcraft

Weapons:
- Heavy turbolaser cannon
- Missile launchers

ALIEN PROFILE
Dugs

Wily, selfish creatures, Dugs have adapted to walk on their hands and use their feet for holding things.

Doge Nakha Urus

The leader of Malastare's Dugs, Doge Urus drives a hard bargain in negotiating a treaty with the Republic, as he knows Palpatine needs his planet's fuel reserves.

PLANET PROFILE
Malastare

This Mid Rim world is controlled by the Dugs, though many three-eyed Gran live there as well. A popular Podracing destination, it is also known for its fuel reserves.

EPISODE HIGHLIGHT

WEAPON PROFILE
Electro-proton Bomb

A new weapon in the Republic arsenal, the electro-proton bomb is designed to disrupt the circuitry of battle droids and Separatist machinery for kilometres from the impact point.

"The most dangerous beast is the beast within."

IT'S WHAT WE'RE CAPABLE OF THAT FRIGHTENS ME.

SYNOPSIS

On Coruscant, Palpatine orders Sionver Boll to kill the captive Zillo Beast, arguing that its military value could hasten the end of the war. Boll attempts to gas the creature, but it breaks free – and races for the Senate Building, determined to kill Palpatine. As the Jedi dispatch stun tanks, Anakin, Padmé, Palpatine and the droids try to escape in Palpatine's shuttle, but are seized by the creature. After gunships arrive with gas bombs, the Zillo Beast succumbs to the poison and falls to its death.

NEWSREEL

A calculated risk. Following a costly victory on the planet Malastare, Chancellor Palpatine orders Jedi Knights Mace Windu and Anakin Skywalker to transport a fearsome Zillo Beast – captured during the battle – back to Coruscant. After seeing that not even a lightsaber could harm the beast, Chancellor Palpatine hopes to unlock the secret of its invulnerability to create new armour for the Republic's clone troopers. Tensions run high as the most dangerous life form in the galaxy touches down on its most populous planet . . . ▪

Model: Slayn & Korpil H-2 executive shuttle

Class: Shuttle

Weapons:
• None

EPISODE HIGHLIGHT

Sionver Boll

Sionver Boll is a brilliant Republic scientist whose experimental bomb brings the Republic a much-needed victory on Malastare. She questions the morality of killing the Zillo Beast for military purposes.

DROID PROFILE
Courier Droid

These hovering droids carry small shipments across Coruscant's cityscape, but can be adapted for almost any situation where a nimble, flying mechanical could be useful — such as drugging a giant beast.

VEHICLE PROFILE
Hover Sled

Model: Loronar X-Alpha heavy cargo sled

Class: Repulsorcraft

Weapons:
• None

PROFILE
Observation Pod

Sionver Boll supervises experiments on the Zillo Beast from a hovering pod much like the repulsorlift pods used in the Senate.

Mas Amedda

Mas Amedda presides over the Senate Chamber during debates, and is tireless in his efforts to advance Palpatine's agenda. Amedda will sweet-talk reluctant Senators, work to persuade them, and bully them if he has to.

NOW THAT'S A CADET TO WATCH.

SYNOPSIS

A Republic frigate carrying young clone trainees docks with Admiral Kilian's Jedi cruiser, accompanied by Anakin and Mace. A new trainee slips away from the group and plants a bomb in Mace's quarters. It's Boba Fett, seeking to avenge the death of his father Jango on Geonosis. When the bomb fails to kill Mace, Boba sabotages the reactor. He then evacuates with the other cadets and is picked up by Aurra Sing in *Slave I*. She tells him to maroon the other cadets, who are then rescued by Anakin and Mace.

Sergeant Fury

An experienced gunnery sergeant, Fury offers the clone cadets hands-on training in space combat, supervising their session in a turbolaser gunner's chair.

TRIVIA

Admiral Kilian is named in honour of Kilian Plunkett, lead designer on *The Clone Wars.*

Jax

A clone cadet with maturity beyond his accelerated years, Jax befriends the Clone Youth Brigade's newest arrival, who goes by the name of Lucky.

NEWSREEL

Calm before the storm! A rare and welcome respite from endless battle awaits Jedi Knights Anakin Skywalker and Mace Windu as they travel through deep space aboard the Jedi cruiser *Endurance*. Preparing to rendezvous with a Republic frigate, the Jedi remain unaware of a deadly peril lying hidden in their midst . . . ∎

EPISODE HIGHLIGHT

WELL, WHAT DO WE HAVE HERE? YOU BOYS LOOK LOST. CONGRATULATIONS, BOBA. JOB WELL DONE.

HIS NAME'S NOT BOBA. HE'S LUCKY.

LUCKY? HA. THAT'S A GOOD ONE.

VEHICLE PROFILE
Endurance

Model: *Venator*-class Star Destroyer

Class: Capital ship

Weapons:
- Heavy turbolasers
- Torpedos
- Fighter complement

WEAPON PROFILE
Turbolaser Cannon

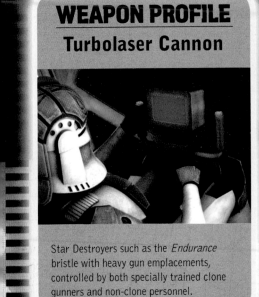

Star Destroyers such as the *Endurance* bristle with heavy gun emplacements, controlled by both specially trained clone gunners and non-clone personnel.

Crasher

A veteran clone sergeant, Crasher keeps a close eye and a tight leash on his Clone Youth Brigade. Crasher talks tough, but he takes great pride in his young clones.

Detonators come in a variety of shapes and sizes, from thermal detonators with deadman's switches to the sophisticated model activated by a laser tripwire that "Lucky" leaves in Mace's quarters.

EPISODE HIGHLIGHT

ADMIRAL, YOU MUST ABANDON SHIP.

NOT A CHANCE.

PROFILE
Clone Youth Brigade

The clones of Crasher's brigade aren't really eleven years old, thanks to Kaminoan secrets of accelerated aging. But whatever their apparent age, they must grow, learn and mature before they are ready for the battlefield.

"Adversity is a friendships truest test."

IS THAT A MANDALORIAN HELMET? WHAT IS THAT DOING HERE?

SYNOPSIS

Exploring the wreckage of the *Endurance*, Mace and Anakin discover that several clones were killed by blaster fire and the assassin is still at large. After the Jedi trigger a booby-trap on the shattered bridge and are buried in debris, R2-D2 holds off Boba Fett and his gang of bounty hunters, then speeds off in a starfighter to get help, with *Slave I* in hot pursuit. Alerted by R2, Ahsoka and Plo Koon rescue Anakin and Mace just before the *Endurance* explodes.

Bossk

A Trandoshan bounty hunter, Bossk is one of many guns-for-hire seeking to profit from the chaos of a war-torn galaxy.

NEWSREEL

Revenge! Boba Fett, son of the notorious bounty hunter Jango Fett, infiltrated a Jedi cruiser in an attempt to assassinate General Mace Windu, the man who killed his father. After a near-miss at Windu's quarters, Boba was forced to destroy the Jedi cruiser and escape with the help of the notorious bounty hunter Aurra Sing. Now, having lost contact with Admiral Kilian when his doomed starship crashed, the Jedi search for survivors with the aid of a Republic rescue ship . . . ■

VEHICLE PROFILE
Slave I

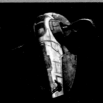

Model: Modified *Firespray*-class attack craft

Class: Space transport

Weapons:
- Laser cannons
- Projectile launcher
- Minelayer

EPISODE HIGHLIGHT

Castas

A Klatooinian bounty hunter, Castas grows tired of taking orders from Aurra Sing. He doesn't mind dirty work, but thinks tangling with the Republic Navy is crazy.

EPISODE HIGHLIGHT

Comet

A member of Commander Wolffe's Wolfpack, Comet helps free Anakin and Mace from the wrecked bridge of the *Endurance*.

ALIEN PROFILE
Klatooinians

Klatooinians are from a desert world in Hutt Space, and many make their living in the galactic underworld as bounty hunters, smugglers and thugs.

R8-B7

Mace Windu's astromech, R8-B7 is more business-like than the brash R2-D2. He meets his end after running afoul of a Gundark.

PROFILE
Hyperdrive Ring

Most starfighters lack faster-than-light engines and use hyperdrive rings to travel across the galaxy, detaching from the ring once they reach their destination.

PROFILE
Wolfpack

Commander Wolffe's squad of clone troopers serves Plo Koon, and are notable for the wolf designs on their helmets as well as their devotion to their Jedi General.

SYNOPSIS

Appearing to the Jedi by hologram, Aurra Sing executes a Republic hostage and threatens to kill the others if Mace doesn't face Boba. With Anakin and Mace still injured, Plo Koon and Ahsoka seek answers in Coruscant's lower levels. Meanwhile, Aurra's gang heads for Florrum, where Aurra kills Castas. Ahsoka learns of Castas's death, and she and Plo race to Florrum. In a pitched battle Boba is captured and Aurra flees, pursued by Ahsoka. The bounty hunter leaps into *Slave I*, but crashes. The hostages are freed and Boba is taken away to answer for what he's done.

SO I SHOULD BEHAVE AS THIS CHILD DOES? I SHOULD SEEK REVENGE?

ALIEN PROFILE
Nautolans

Nautolans are native to Glee Anselm in the Mid Rim. They are excellent swimmers and have a superb sense of smell.

NEWSREEL

Lethal trackdown! The young Boba Fett has taken the law into his own hands and made two attempts on the life of Mace Windu, the Jedi Master who killed his father! Boba's mentor, bounty hunter Aurra Sing, has taken three Republic officers hostage in an effort to force Windu to face Boba on their terms – a tactic that does not sit well with the young vigilante . . . ∎

EPISODE HIGHLIGHT

Boba Fett

An unaltered clone of Jango Fett, Boba was orphaned by his father's death on Geonosis, and seeks to avenge him by killing Mace Windu. Yet he struggles with his conscience when innocents get in the way.

ALIEN PROFILE
Kowakian Monkey-Lizards

Some find the shrill laughter and antics of these sly little beasts amusing, while others consider monkey-lizards vermin. The pirate Hondo Ohnaka keeps a pair as his gang's mascots.

WEAPON PROFILE
Bossk's Gun

Formally known as a Relby-v10 micro grenade launcher, this long-barrelled rifle is used to deadly effect by Bossk when hunting his prey.

Admiral Kilian

The commander of the *Endurance*, the proud Kilian finds himself Boba's hostage, and tries to appeal to the conflicted young clone's sense of honour.

Fong Do

A Nautolan who frequents Coruscant's more disreputable establishments, Fong Do likes a good bit of gossip as much as the next thug. Wait till you hear what just happened to his old pal Castas out on Florrum . . .

WEAPON PROFILE
Dart Launchers

Bounty hunters are full of surprises, and Aurra Sing is no exception – the toes of her boots conceal deadly spring-loaded darts.

EPISODE HIGHLIGHT

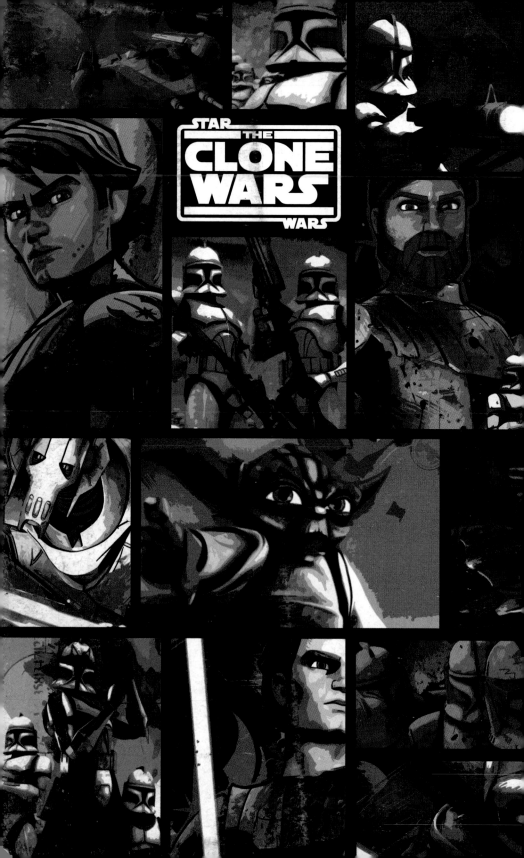